# FAMILY PAIN

RECOVERY
DISCOVERY

# FAMILY PAIN

*Healing for Adult Children of Alcoholic
and Other Dysfunctional Families*

*Randy Reynolds & David Lynn*

ZondervanPublishingHouse
*Grand Rapids, Michigan*

*A Division of HarperCollinsPublishers*

Family Pain
Copyright © 1992 by Randy Reynolds and David Lynn

Requests for information should be addressed to:
Zondervan Publishing House
Grand Rapids, Michigan 49530

ISBN 0-310-57331-9

Edited by Linda Vanderzalm
Cover design by Lecy Design
Cover photo by Dan Hummel
Interior design by Ann Cherryman

Printed in the United States of America

92  93  94  95  96  97 / DP / 10  9  8  7  6  5  4  3  2  1

# CONTENTS

*This book is dedicated to all those adult children of alcoholics and other dysfunctional families who have realized that something is not quite right in their lives. With this Recovery Discovery workbook, you have begun a journey to recovery. May you experience the grace and peace that only Jesus Christ can provide in your recovery journey.*

# Introduction

This book is about pain, anxiety, and conflict. But pain, anxiety, and conflict are not its destination. We have written this Recovery Discovery workbook to offer hope and help for adults who grew up in alcoholic and other dysfunctional families.

As you work through this book, your heart will ache from distressing memories. You will get angry. But most of all, you will begin a journey of recovery from a painful past that has haunted your adult life. The book has grown out of our experiences working with adult children of alcoholics and other dysfunctional families. Not everything in this workbook may apply to you. Take what you need. Not every child of a dysfunctional family must work through the same issues. We have tried to identify patterns and core issues that we see again and again.

We have organized this workbook around the fruit of the Spirit described in Galatians 5:22–23: love, joy, peace, patience, kindness, goodness, faithfulness, gentleness, and self-control. Each chapter examines one of the fruits as it relates to the struggles of adult children of dysfunctional families.

The lack of recovery in Christian families is often a result of the rules learned in the dysfunctional family. These rules, like "Don't talk," "Don't feel," or "Don't trust," wield power even when the alcohol is eliminated for a generation.

When an unhealthy family becomes healthy, however, there is a change in atmosphere. The apostle Paul attributes this change to the difference between living under the law as opposed to living under the Spirit. Families who live under law have more problems with relationships, compulsions, and addictions; whereas families who live under grace enjoy the fruit of the Spirit. Their behavior can be viewed on a continuum (see chart on next page).

## HOW TO USE THIS WORKBOOK

Each chapter consists of five sections. *Recovery Focus* highlights the issues the chapter will discuss. *Recovery Information* explains the issues with which you may be wrestling, while the *Recovery Probers* gives questions that help you take a personal look at your own place in the recovery process. The *Recovery Guide* is designed to help you explore Scripture passages that give perspective to the recovery issues and to point you to God as a source of wisdom and strength. At the end of

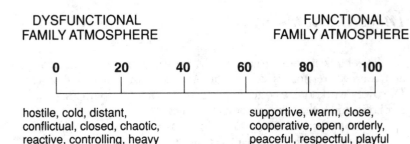

each chapter, the *Recovery Goals* gives you a chance to formulate goals that you need to work on as you move toward wholeness and recovery.

Take the time to write out your answers to the questions in each chapter. Reflect carefully on your feelings and beliefs. Pray, asking God to use this workbook as a tool for your recovery. Then discuss your insights and feelings with someone—ideally with a small group that will study this workbook together.

If you are part of such a group, speak up. Share your thoughts with the group. Look to the others for help and support. Learn from them as they share their stories and struggles. Pray together, depending on God to work in your lives. And rejoice together as you grow and find wholeness in your recovery.

If you aren't able to be part of a small group, talk over your recovery process with a trusted pastor, counselor, or balanced and trustworthy friend. Share your responses and questions with that other person. Ask him or her to pray for you regularly.

Remember, recovery is not instant. Rather, your recovery will be a lifelong adventure of growing closer to God, to others, and to yourself. Welcome to the journey.

# 1.

# It Won't Happen to Me

## RECOVERY FOCUS

- Identify what type of family you grew up in.
- Review your family tree as a recovery step.
- Identify the effect of your family's dysfunction on you.

## RECOVERY INFORMATION

You survived! And you aren't alone. Millions of other people also survived growing up in an alcoholic or other dysfunctional home. Statistics tell us that one of every seven to ten children grows up in a home with an alcoholic parent. And each of these children grows up to be an adult child of an alcoholic.

These statistics do not include all those people who grew up in families with parents who were problem drinkers, with grandparents who were alcoholics, or with parents who physically, sexually, or emotionally abused them.

### TYPES OF FAMILIES

Alcoholic and dysfunctional families vary. As you read through the discussion of four types of families, decide which family type best describes your family of origin.

*The wet-alcoholic family.* If you grew up in a wet-alcoholic family, your family system was organized around alcohol. One or both parents drank all the time (or were drug addicted) or drank for long periods interspersed with periods of no drinking. Other relatives like grandparents or aunts and uncles may have been alcoholics, although this isn't always the case.

Read this list of characteristics, checking those that describe your family life.

☐ You worried about a parent's pattern of drinking.

☐ You avoided bringing friends over to your house for fear that your parent may have been drinking.

☐ You fantasized that your parent would stop drinking.

☐ You felt it was your fault that your parent drank.

☐ You thought your parent had a problem with drinking.

☐ The holidays were more tense for you because of your parent's drinking.

☐ You took care of a parent who had been drinking.

☐ Promises your parent made to you were broken because of that parent's drinking.

☐ You fought with your non-drinking parent or your brothers and sisters about your drinking parent's drinking.

☐ Your parents fought about your drinking parent's drinking.

☐ Friends have asked you if your parent was an alcoholic.

☐ You have felt that one or both of your parents were alcoholic.

If you checked several of these statements, you probably grew up with an alcoholic parent.

*The dry-alcoholic family.* If you grew up in a dry-alcoholic family, your drinking (or drug-using) parent stopped using alcohol, but the family continued to function as if the alcohol were present. This is called the "dry-drunk syndrome." The family is still affected by the *ism* of alcoholism. All the self-defeating attitudes and behaviors that developed to cope with active drinking persist. Manny's father quit drinking when he was twelve years old. His mother divorced his father when Manny was fourteen, but the family, even in the absence of his father, continued to act in ways that were alcoholic.

*The no-alcohol-alcoholic family.* If you grew up in a no-alcohol-alcoholic family, the alcoholic person was removed from your family by one or more generations. But the adult children of alcoholic issues have endured. The *ism* of alcoholism continues to function even though the drinking behavior has been removed generationally. This dynamic is especially prevalent with Christian families. The conversion frees the family from the alcohol but not from the rules for living learned in the alcoholic family.

Many grandchildren of alcoholics report that they were told their families were better than other families. "I kept getting the message that our family was perfect," said Jennifer, "and this was really confusing because I knew something was wrong. I just couldn't put my finger on what it was." The adult children of alcoholic parents have done this in the hope and with the belief that the family now is better because alcohol is not actively used. This gives Christian parents who are adult children of alcoholics the feeling that they have overcome their alcoholic childhood families. Their conversion has given them permission to isolate from their drinking family without working through their adult-children-of-alcoholics' issues. And these issues are passed on to kids, creating a new generation of adult children of alcoholics.

*The no-alcohol-dysfunctional family.* A study reported in the *Counseling Psychology Quarterly* 2, no. 4 (1989) compared adult children of alcoholics with adult children who grew up in families with other dysfunctions, such as parental chronic mental illness. Both groups were given psychological tests that measured depression, irrational beliefs, and personality disorders. Not surprisingly, the research revealed not only similarities between the two groups but also a difference between them and a population of normal adults. Growing up in a dysfunctional home is quite similar to growing up in an alcoholic home.

When we use the term "adult children," we refer to adults who grew up in alcoholic or other dysfunctional families, whether that be a wet-alcoholic family, a dry-alcoholic family, a no-alcohol-alcoholic family, or a no-alcohol-dysfunctional family.

## EFFECTS OF GROWING UP IN AN ALCOHOLIC FAMILY

Growing up in a dysfunctional family, whether the contributing factor to the dysfunction was alcoholism or something else, does not doom you to a life of troubles and heartaches. Many people raised in abusive homes have overcome this adversity, leading productive and well-adjusted lives. Others have grown stronger because of the difficulties they were required to overcome in order to survive in their homes.

But growing up in an atmosphere of conflict, inconsistency, and confusion often takes its toll. Adults who grew up in dysfunctional families are more likely to experience relationship problems, divorce, alcohol and drug abuse, low self-esteem, eating disorders, depression, and dissatisfaction with life, to name only a few issues.

If you grew up in a family system organized around alcohol or another dysfunction, you may not even have realized this fact because no immediate family member actively drank. You knew something was different in your family. You observed other families and knew that your family wasn't like theirs. Perhaps for years you have tried to put this thought out of your mind. But now your life is not operating the way you think it should. And that awareness has brought you to this Recovery Discovery workbook.

You can change. Conditions can get better in your life. You can be the pivotal person who breaks the dysfunctional pattern that has proved so destructive to your family. With God's help and grace, recovery can be yours.

Interestingly, a study was conducted to determine how alcoholism affected evangelical Christians. The research reported in the *Journal of Psychology and Theology* (Fall 1989) compared Christian adult children of alcoholics with Christian adults who had not grown up in alcoholic homes. The research focused on personality characteristics and core issues for adult children of alcoholics. It was found that the evangelicals from alcoholic homes had significantly more problems with repressing their feelings, depression, mistrust, guilt, and self-blame than evangelicals not from alcoholic homes.

## YOUR FAMILY TREE

Examining your family tree for evidence of alcoholism and other problems such as depression or chronic mental illness can help you better understand how your family system became dysfunctional. Often, adult children have a distorted view of their families.

The following family tree exercise can provide you with valuable insight into your family background. The family tree activity also helps you acknowledge your past. Much of the information about your family has been hidden, with family problems minimized. One of the family rules you learned growing up was "Don't talk about the real issue." And the real issue in your family was your father's drinking or your mother's depression or the sexual abuse inflicted on you by your stepfather or whatever.

This family tree activity is not intended to force you to become preoccupied with your past or to focus on self-awareness or self-actualization. A preoccupation with the self will only keep you stuck in self-defeating behaviors. Rather, this activity helps you to break the "Don't-talk" rule, moving you out of the denial so prevalent in your childhood family so that you can clearly examine your self-defeating behaviors.

## DIRECTIONS FOR FILLING IN YOUR FAMILY TREE

Box #1—Write your name. On the lines surrounding your name, place the names of your brothers and sisters. If you are married, place your spouse's name in the dotted box below your name. If you have been divorced, place the name of your former spouse next to the dotted box. If you are not married but presently in a relationship, place that person's name next to the dotted box. Put the names of your children on the dotted lines below the dotted box designated for your spouse.

Box #2—Write your father's name. To the left of this box, write the names of all your paternal aunts and uncles.

Box #3—Write your mother's name. To the right of this box, write the names of all your maternal aunts and uncles.

Box #4—Write your paternal grandfather's name. Above this box, put the names of his brothers and sisters (your paternal great aunts/uncles).

Box #5—Write your paternal grandmother's name. Above this box, put the names of her brothers and sisters (your paternal great aunts/uncles).

Box #6—Write your maternal grandfather's name. Above this box, put the names of his brothers and sisters (your maternal great aunts/uncles).

Box #7—Write your maternal grandmother's name. Above this box, put the names of her brothers and sisters (your maternal great aunts/uncles).

Place an X in the boxes and on the lines of each person who was or is an alcoholic.

Don't be surprised if you can't complete your family tree. Be as thorough as possible. You may have to do a little research, asking relatives to help you complete the task. And remember the "Don't-talk" rule applies to them as well. Don't be surprised if relatives say things like, "Uncle Harry did have a little drinking problem." Actually Harry was an outright drunk.

You can also examine additional issues in your family history such as drug addiction, physical abuse, sexual abuse, depression, smoking, food addictions (overeating, anorexia, bulimia), codependency, mental illness, or divorce. Create your own coding system for the issues you wish to examine within your family tree.

Once you have coded your family tree, go back and review it carefully. What patterns emerged? How have these patterns affected your relationships? Your children? Many people are surprised at the extent of alcoholism and other mental illness prevalent in their parents, grandparents, aunts and uncles, spouses, and children. If you extended

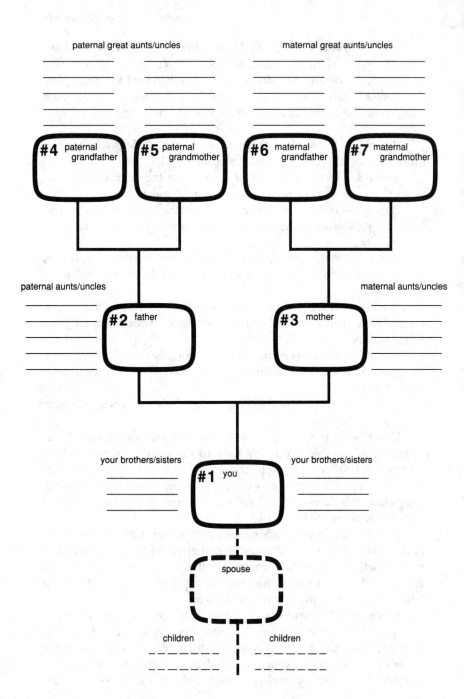

your family tree to include cousins and great grandparents, you would see additional problems.

Alberto reviewed his family tree and was surprised to learn how many women he had dated had came from alcoholic homes. His former wife had also come from a family of alcoholics. His mother was an adult child of an alcoholic, with her father and grandfather both alcoholics. His father was a dry drunk. He had one brother who was most likely addicted to marijuana and a sister who had married an alcoholic. Another brother had married an adult child of an alcoholic. Alberto was not an alcoholic but could see how the alcoholism in his family had influenced the self-defeating behaviors in his own life.

## RECOVERY PROBERS

1. Which family type best describes your childhood family?


2. If you grew up in a family indirectly affected by alcohol (dry-alcoholic or no-alcohol-alcoholic family system), what do you believe you have in common with those who grew up in a family more directly affected by alcohol?


3. How do you feel growing up in a dysfunctional family not affected by alcohol is similar to growing up in a family organized around alcoholism?


4. What observations did you make as you completed your family tree?


5. What surprised you the most about your family tree?

6. **What feelings kept presenting themselves as you completed your family tree?**

7. **How can the completion of your family tree contribute to your recovery?**

## RECOVERY GUIDE

So I say, live by the Spirit, and you will not gratify the desires of the sinful nature. (Galatians 5:16)

### Read Galatians 5:19–21.

The acts of the sinful nature can be loosely divided into four groups:
- sexual issues (sexual immorality, impurity, and debauchery)
- following false gods (idolatry and witchcraft)
- relationship struggles (hatred, discord, jealousy, fits of rage, selfish ambition, dissensions, factions, and envy)
- addictions (drunkenness, orgies, and the like)

Each of these groups represents problems prevalent in families with alcoholism or other dysfunctions.

1. **List examples of sexual issues found in your family tree (sexual permissiveness, incest, homosexuality).**

2. **List examples of the following of false gods in your family tree (money, work, religions, power, satanism, atheism).**

3. **List examples of relationship struggles found in your family tree (conflict, violence, tension, anger, emotional abuse, divorce).**

4. **List examples of addictions found in your family tree (alcohol, drugs, tobacco, sex, eating disorders, gambling, relationships, religion).**

## Read this family tree excerpted from 1 Kings 15 to 2 Kings 3.

Abijah committed all the sins his father had done before him; his heart was not fully devoted to the Lord his God, as the heart of David his forefather had been. . . . Nadab did evil in the eyes of the Lord. . . . Baasha did evil in the eyes of the Lord. . . . Elah was getting drunk and Zimri came in, struck him down and killed him. . . . Zimri died, because of the sins he had committed, doing evil in the eyes of the Lord and walking in the ways of Jeroboam. . . . Ahab son of Omri did more evil in the eyes of the Lord than any of those before him. . . . Ahaziah son of Ahab did evil in the eyes of the Lord, because he walked in the ways of his father and mother and in the ways of Jeroboam. . . . Joram son of Ahab did evil in the eyes of the Lord, but not as his father and mother had done. He got rid of the sacred stone of Baal that his father had made. Nevertheless he clung to the sins of Jeroboam.

This short genealogical tree reveals that, for the most part, the sins of the fathers were passed from one generation to another. However, bright spots appeared periodically in the record, giving us hope that the dysfunctional-family rules we have inherited do not have to be followed.

1. **How do you feel you have been affected by your family tree?**

**2. What bright spots exist in your family tree?**

**3. How committed are you to gaining victory over the dysfunction found in your family tree?**

## RECOVERY GOALS

"But if they will confess their sins and the sins of their fathers—their treachery against me and their hostility toward me, which made me hostile toward them so that I sent them into the land of their enemies—then when their uncircumcised hearts are humbled and they pay for their sin, I will remember my covenant." (Leviticus 26:40–42).

The family tree activity has helped you fulfill this biblical principle of confession of your own sins as well as those of past generations. Review your family tree again, asking God to cleanse you of your sins and the sins of your fathers and mothers.

# 2.    I Look for Love in All the Wrong Places: Love

## RECOVERY FOCUS

- Identify your role in your family.
- Reshape your role in a constructive direction.
- Grow in Christ through your role.

## RECOVERY INFORMATION

You grew up with the desire to feel significant. You have a unique position in your family as well as a unique contribution to the functioning of your family. Your role helped you feel loved.

Firstborn children begin life as only children. They receive the undivided attention of their parents. When the second child arrives, the first child must work harder to maintain that first position. The second child will quickly figure out how to be different from the first child in order to keep the parents' attention.

As each child is born, a new role is created to help the child find a place of significance within the family. Rudolf Dreikurs, a follower of Alfred Adler, popularized the family-constellation model, which forms the basis of many self-help books that analyze family constellations and their effect on our development.

Growing up in an alcoholic or other dysfunctional family amplifies these roles. Children growing up amidst dysfunction must over-exaggerate their roles in order to find significance and survive in their family. A family role becomes a defensive pattern of behaviors used to seek love and significance.

Karen Black and Sharon Wegscheider, experts in the field of alcoholism studies, propose four basic family roles exaggerated by the alcoholic and other dysfunctional family systems.

- the responsible one/hero

- the acting-out one/scapegoat
- the adjuster/lost child
- the placater/mascot

Let's look at each role separately. As you are reading each of the descriptions, reflect on which role best describes your experience.

## THE RESPONSIBLE ONE/HERO

The oldest child most often plays the responsible one/hero role, although when siblings are born close together, the second child sometimes becomes the hero. The hero gets positive attention through over-achieving. Heroes do well in school or excel in sports. This does provide a sense of self-worth for the hero as well as the family. "We aren't doing so bad" is a common parental response because of the child that plays this role. Heroes learn the family values—caregiving or achieving or cleaning the house, for example—and do well in fulfilling them.

Many times children who are heroes appear to have it all together. Heroes grow up believing they have to make up for the deficits of the family. Heroes learn early in life that being really good pays off in attention and approval. Heroes strive to put the needs of the family before their own. Heroes aim to please through success.

## THE ACTING-OUT ONE/SCAPEGOAT

Generally, the second child becomes the acting-out one/scapegoat. Children in this role get attention and significance by being oppositional. Since heroes have already captured the "doing-everything-right" role (over-functioning), scapegoats gain recognition through doing everything wrong (under-functioning). They break the rules either aggressively or passively. Scapegoats children are difficult to discipline. They are stubborn, preferring to do things their way. The negative, attention-getting behavior of the scapegoat focuses the blame away from the alcoholism or dysfunction and onto the child.

Scapegoats stay away from the family, preferring instead to spend more and more time with peers. Choosing friends who are like-minded, they are more likely to get into trouble at school, become pregnant, shoplift, smoke, and begin experimenting with alcohol and drugs in early adolescence. The heroes bring praise to the family while the scapegoats bring disappointment and dishonor. "You're always causing problems for our family" is a familiar theme for them.

The scapegoats find themselves fighting more and more with

family members. They rebel against doing the chores. They focus on perceived injustices and have problems with authority figures. They miss curfews. When physical abuse occurs, the scapegoats usually catch the brunt of it. They are more likely to fight for their rights in the family. They act out of frustration and hurt, but their behavior only brings more hurt from their parents and often leads to low self-esteem.

Scapegoats tend to be more realistic in their perspective of the family. They also have more courage to be themselves and confront a sick family system. They are often the first to find help for themselves.

## THE ADJUSTER/LOST CHILD

Third children usually find their place in the adjuster/lost child role. They become invisible in the family. Lost children find the family easier to handle if they spend time in their rooms, away from the tension. They find their love and significance by not making waves. They want to avoid creating problems within and for the family. When tension and anxiety flare up in the family, they draw into themselves for protection. Lost children do not usually get close to their parents. They never learn to form lasting relationships, and as a result they don't learn simple social skills like communication. They can blend into the woodwork whether at home, school, or church. Lost children tend to have more depression as adults, often feeling unwanted. However, they are good at adapting, fitting in, and learning the rules.

## THE PLACATER/MASCOT

By the time the placater/mascot arrives in the family, vying for love and attention requires a more direct approach than that of the lost child. Mascots learn to generate positive attention for themselves and relief for the family by entertaining. They goof off, act up, and clown around in humorous ways that leave the family laughing. They can also relieve tension in negative ways, such as acting helpless, being hyperactive, or creating accidents. Any of these behavior patterns gets them the attention they desperately seek and keeps the family functioning. Mascots often are told they are "so cute." Mascots often miss out in school; they are too busy goofing off. What they miss in their studies they make up for in their social skills by manipulating the teacher and having the class cover for them.

Mascots comfort others in ways other than humor. Many of them become great listeners, very sensitive and caring. They meet the emotional needs of others well but do not take care of themselves. They spend their childhoods smoothing things over for everybody else.

## MULTIPLE ROLES

Due to the anxiety-filled nature of the dysfunctional family system, children often take on multiple roles. Heroes can give up trying so hard and become scapegoats. Or scapegoats may be neglected and become lost children. Combining roles is a survival technique used by family members to defend themselves. These roles are carried into adult life, creating problems because they are overdeveloped.

Children can change their roles, especially as a result of change in their families. A divorce, suicide, job loss, remarriage, or the creation of a blended family can all trigger a change in roles. The role change doesn't occur immediately but over a period of time. By the time children reach adulthood, they may have experienced two or more roles.

It's important to remember that all families have these basic roles. However, if you grew up in a dysfunctional family, these roles became exaggerated, causing you to grow up with deeply ingrained patterns of defensive behaviors. The behavior patterns helped you survive the unhealthy family atmosphere in which you were raised, but now they create problems for you as an adult.

Dreikurs taught that problems in personality development occur when the family atmosphere is one of discouragement and lack of cooperation, both hallmarks of alcoholic and other dysfunctional families. From birth you began acting in very purposive ways in order to survive in your family. Your role provided you with behavior patterns that appeared at the time to be a workable means of living.

## MOVING INTO ADULTHOOD

Our roles follow us into adulthood, for good or for bad. If your role has created problems for you as an adult, you can reshape it in ways that are productive and helpful to your spiritual growth. The roles themselves are not all bad; each has its strengths too. It's the *exaggeration* of roles that has created difficulties for you.

The key is finding a balance. How can you maximize your strengths and minimize your weaknesses? How can you function within your role in positive ways? Let's examine each role and gain a better understanding of how your role affects you today and how you can reshape that role in a positive direction.

*The responsible one/hero.* No matter what heroes do, it's never good enough. Heroes' over-functioning doesn't make the family any healthier, but heroes go on over-functioning, taking on more responsibility. And they take this dynamic into their adult lives.

Heroes are very good at taking care of others. After all, that's how they found love and significance in their families. But heroes take care of others at the expense of their own needs and problems. Their own problems never get addressed because they are too busy looking after others or making it seem that they have it together.

Heroes find it extremely difficult to relax. They have spent so much time being responsible that they can't turn it off. This makes them candidates for stress-related illness and burnout. (For help with stress, see *Stress Relief,* a workbook in this Recovery Discovery series.)

Heroes often feel used in their church life. They volunteer for everything and are easily taken advantage of in their quest to serve the Lord. Heroes have difficulty trusting and relying on God because they feel that it is irresponsible to trust anyone except themselves.

Alcohol and other compulsions like overworking can easily overcome heroes, who look to compulsions to offer relief for the depression and anxiety they feel. Heroes are often resistant to change. Their self-defeating behaviors are difficult to admit since they have spent their lives appearing successful.

Heroes can achieve more if they can relax and examine their lives. Once heroes learn to reflect more on their over-functioning, they can turn their productivity toward positive ends while not neglecting their own needs or their family's needs for emotional closeness and time together.

*The acting-out one/scapegoat.* When acting-out ones/scapegoats enter adulthood, they often find themselves at a disadvantage. They most likely have not done well in school. They often abuse alcohol and other drugs and are constantly angry. Scapegoats have problems with authority figures, whether that authority is the boss, the police, a counselor, or a pastor. As a result, they will often lose jobs, miss promotions, or get in trouble with the law. They continue their rebellious role, which only adds to their list of problems. Feeling more at home with other rebels, they have dysfunctional friendships or few or no friendships at all.

Scapegoats feel judged by the church. They believe the church is always pointing a condemning finger at them. They see themselves as victims who don't measure up to other people's standards. They are great at making excuses and conning other people. They use their acting out to draw attention to themselves even though they hate this negative attention.

Scapegoats usually are the first to find help for their troubles. Unlike the heroes, they are more aware of their family's problems as well as their own difficulties. They are assertive and concerned about the injustices they see in the church and in the world. If it's channeled in the right direction, their anger, rebellious spirit, and energy can be productive in fighting injustice. They can have a vibrant, alive relationship with God and others once they learn to rest in God's authority. They can learn to keep the rules once they realize that God gave rules for their protection.

*The adjuster/lost child.* Adjusters/lost children find adult relationships difficult because they lack social skills. Because they don't value their own thoughts, feelings, and desires, they often have difficulty making assertive decisions. If they are asked what they want to do, they will often respond, "I don't know, what do you want to do?" They need to learn communication and assertiveness skills.

Lost children feel that if they don't create problems, they're doing okay. They suffer in their careers because they have difficulty taking risks and getting ahead. In their desire to protect themselves, they avoid conflict and withdraw, only to feel miserable and alone. They miss out on the enjoyment of life.

The aloneness and isolation often experienced by lost children as adults can be turned into a spiritual opportunity. They can actively seek God during these times of solitude and quiet.

*The placater/mascot.* As adults, placaters/mascots are the life of the party. In restaurants they are hilarious. In tense situations at work or at home, their wit breaks the tension. But this wit and humor also cover their pain. They have difficulty honestly confronting their issues because they can always divert attention by clowning around.

Mascots as adults often find themselves emotionally, mentally, and spiritually impoverished because they have focused so much of their attention on their social skills. They deal with tension and pain by distracting themselves and others, hoping it will go away.

They need to develop their mental, emotional, and spiritual selves. They need to use their social skills productively. They need to face their pain and conflict constructively. Placaters need to take life more seriously, to grow up, to take responsibility. They need to learn to face issues rather than getting distracted and denying problems.

## RECOVERY PROBERS

1. What is the predominant role you played growing up in your family?

2. What other roles, if any, did you play growing up?

3. How did your role help you survive in your family?

4. What roles were played by your siblings? How did you relate to them?

5. What benefits came from the roles played by others in your family?

6. How has your role helped you make positive contributions as an adult?

7. How has your role created problems for you as an adult?

8. How can you reshape your role so that it works for you rather than against you?

# RECOVERY GUIDE

But the fruit of the Spirit is love. (Galatians 5:22)

## Read Philippians 1:9–10.

Paul's prayer reveals that we need both true knowledge and true insight for love to grow and flourish in our relationships. We need God's perspective on our attitudes and behaviors and on the attitudes and behaviors of those around us in order to continue to grow in him and in our relationship with others. "Depth of insight" refers to the practical choices we need to make within our relationships.

Knowledge and insight produce right living. If we are willing to pursue a relationship with God through Jesus Christ, we can more clearly see what is really going on and we can thus more appropriately live out our lives in relationship to others and actively work at reshaping our lives.

1. How are you growing closer to Jesus Christ?

2. Are you involved in relationships with other believers who are trustworthy and who will provide you with honest feedback about your role?

3. How can you grow in your knowledge and insight?

## Read Matthew 11:28–30.

1. Christ calls us into a relationship with him. Our burdens we acquired growing up with alcoholism and dysfunction can be laid at his feet. He can reshape our lives to be more like his. How willing are you to follow Christ?

2. Can you accept by faith that Christ's burdens are lighter than the ones you now carry inside of yourself?

3. What can you do to take Christ's yoke on you and learn from him?

**Read Philippians 3:12–14.**

1. The apostle Paul says you can lay aside your past and focus on what is before you—your recovery in Jesus Christ. How will you begin to put the past behind you?

2. How will you keep your recovery focused on your issues?

## RECOVERY GOALS

You can choose to reorder your priorities in such a way that you focus on the strengths of your role or roles. Right now choose one thing you can do to live out your role in a more productive manner. You can make this choice by completing the sentences that apply to you:

1. As the responsible one/hero I can

2. As the acting-out one/scapegoat I can

3. As the adjuster/lost child I can

4. As the placater/mascot I can

# 3.

# I Wish I Could Be Happy: Joy

## RECOVERY FOCUS

- Overcome the five dysfunctional-family rules.
- Recognize the defense mechanisms that can hinder your recovery.
- Find joy in Christ.

## RECOVERY INFORMATION

God wants you to know joy in your life. But joy seems to elude you. You have sometimes experienced it, especially if you are a Christian. But for the most part, joy is a foreign concept. You may have read books about happiness, heard sermons about the abundant Christian life, and ordered tapes that teach successful living. But you don't experience joy.

One of the things that can rob you of joy is the set of rules you learned in your family. All families create rules that help the family maintain stability and communication, preserve family values, and keep order. If families didn't have rules, chaos would reign. These family rules aren't written down like the Ten Commandments; they're passed down from one generation to another through modeling behaviors of previous generations. Here are some examples of rules that families create and communicate by how they live out their family lives:

- Share with others.
- Always mind your manners.
- We don't need to talk about that.
- Don't bring shame to the family.
- You don't really feel that way.
- We work out our problems by talking.
- Love your neighbor as yourself.
- Don't show your anger.
- Always go to church.

Some of these rules are healthy while others are not. Sharon Wegscheider points out in her book *Another Chance: Hope and Health for the Alcoholic Family* that functional families have healthy, flexible rules. Dysfunctional families live by unhealthy, rigid rules. The more dysfunctional the family, the more rigid and unhealthy the rules by which they live out family life.

In the dysfunctional family system, rules protect family members from the pain and confusion created by the dysfunction. The rules are an attempt to manage the chaos. And they do help people survive life in a dysfunctional family. But the rules do not work in adult life. And they rob you of the joy God wants you to experience.

Let's take a look at five of the negative rules that govern many dysfunctional families.

## THE NO-PROBLEM RULE: DON'T TALK ABOUT REAL ISSUES

To keep the focus off the real problem—the alcoholism or dysfunctional behavior—you learned not to talk about what you saw happening in the family. Talking about it would only create more stress and anxiety. Besides, if the family had ever openly discussed the real problem, they would have had to make difficult changes. Therefore, they avoided discussing it.

You grew up believing that you had to solve your problems by yourself. You felt you couldn't share your real problems with others because they may not have believed you or they may have used them against you. As a result, you have difficulty asking for help, believing instead that you are the only one with the solution to your problems. The family tree activity found in chapter 1 provided you with a chance to break this rule.

## THE FEELINGS RULE: DON'T FEEL

The open sharing of feelings is a threat to the dysfunctional family system. Like not talking about the real issues, not feeling maintains the status quo of alcoholism. You had to stuff your feelings to protect yourself from the pain you felt. If you had allowed yourself to feel, you would have suffered an emotional overload.

You learned that feelings were uncomfortable, even bad, so you cut them off. You learned to avoid your feelings. Another promise broken—disappointment. Dad slapped you around—fear. You got blamed for Mom's condition—guilt. Dad showed up drunk at your school play—embarrassment. Hurt, pain, confusion, hate, worry, suffering, shame. Often you were told to avoid your feelings. Your family did not validate your feelings; instead they discounted them and reacted against them, telling you, "You can't feel like that" or "Why would you feel like that?"

## THE RELATIONSHIP RULE: DON'T TRUST

You learned not to trust your senses (don't talk), even though they clearly identified a problem in your family. You learned not to trust your feelings (don't feel), since your family did not validate them. And you learned not to trust others. Your parents, at least the dysfunctional ones, were not emotionally available for you on a regular basis. So who could you depend on? Trust requires a measure of security that wasn't present in your home. You never knew how crazy your mom was going to act or how drunk your dad was going to be. So you learned to do the sensible thing and not trust.

The dishonesty that marks most dysfunctional homes also prevented you from learning to trust. Dishonesty lets the dysfunctional person avoid his or her problem. Dishonesty allows the family to pretend that everything is all right. It keeps the family operating on a daily basis, but it only feeds the dysfunction and hinders trust from growing.

## THE ISOLATION RULE: DON'T GET CLOSE

When you grew up, it was hard for you to get close to other people because you were always afraid they would find out the truth about your family. You maybe had friends, attended church, or got involved in clubs, but you couldn't get too close. Even now you may have difficulty with intimacy. You feel lonely and anxious even with a group of friends and acquaintances.

This pattern of isolation thwarted outside influence or help. In spite of your family's problems, you were loyal to your family, and your family's us-against-them" mentality not only prevented anyone from getting close, but also kept them from making significant change.

## THE SELF-IMAGE RULE: DON'T FEEL GOOD ABOUT YOURSELF

The result of growing up in a family environment that discounted your feelings, that forced you to deny your instincts about what you saw happening, and that caused you to lose trust in others can only be one thing: self-blame. You begin to believe that something must be wrong with you. You feel different. Even when you feel good about yourself, you don't trust the feeling; you wonder when it's going to end.

Have you ever wondered why you involve yourself in relationships with other unhealthy people? These rules partly explain your choice of friends. Your unhealthy friends follow the same rules for life that you learned, and so you feel comfortable around them.

If you don't work to overcome the negative rules you learned as a child, you may easily fall into compulsive behavior patterns. Adult children of dysfunctional families are some of the most compulsive people in our society.

Read over the following list of behaviors and rate each one by the effect it has had on you. Place a 0 in the box if you are not affected by this behavior, a 1 if you are somewhat affected, and a 2 if you are greatly affected by this behavior.

- [ ] Smoking
- [ ] Overwork
- [ ] Religiosity
- [ ] Perfectionism
- [ ] Explosive anger
- [ ] Addiction to crisis
- [ ] Compulsive gambling
- [ ] Compulsive shopping
- [ ] Compulsive exercising
- [ ] Codependent relationships
- [ ] Physical problems (hypochondria)
- [ ] Addiction to or abuse of alcohol or drugs
- [ ] Eating disorders such overeating, bulimia, or anorexia
- [ ] Sexual compulsions or addictions like masturbation, pornography, or other sexual acting-out behaviors

## OVERCOMING THE RULES

One recovery process that can significantly help you overcome these dysfunctional-family rules as well as stimulate your spiritual growth is the twelve-step approach. Popularized by Alcoholics Anonymous, the twelve-step recovery program is now used by many recovery programs: Al-Anon, Codependents Anonymous, and Adult Children of Alcoholics, to name a few.

The twelve-step program for family members of alcoholics is Al-

Anon. Some Al-Anon groups are designed specifically for people who grew up with parents and grandparents who were alcoholics or drug addicts. If you've never attended Al-Anon meetings, plan to do that. You will find phone numbers listed in the white pages of your telephone book.

A twelve-step approach to recovery is not therapy, although it can be very therapeutic. The emphasis of a twelve-step program is support and healing through community and the examining of the Twelve Steps. Although the Twelve Steps themselves have a spiritual component, not every twelve-step group is overtly Christian. Try to find a group that is soundly Christian, avoiding those that espouse New Age thinking, which can adversely affect your recovery. You can find out about these groups by calling your local information and referral service or by talking with a pastor or local Christian counselor.

## RECOVERY PROBERS

1. **What is the connection between your childhood in an alcoholic or other dysfunctional family and the absence of joy in your life today?**

2. **In what ways did the "Don't-talk-about-real-issues" rule operate in your family?**

3. **In what ways did the "Don't-feel" rule operate in your family?**

4. **In what ways did the "Don't-trust" rule operate in your family?**

5. In what ways did the "Don't-get-close" rule operate in your family?

6. In what ways did the "Don't-feel-good-about-yourself" rule operate in your family?

7. How has your avoidance of feelings hindered or hurt your growth and development?

8. How are feelings useful?

9. How have the "Don't-trust" and "Don't-get-close" rules affected your handling of friendships? Of intimate relationships?

10. What compulsions have you developed in order to cover the pain and anxiety in your life?

## RECOVERY GUIDE

But the fruit of the Spirit is . . . joy. (Galatians 5:22)

The Bible describes joy in three basic contexts. One is the joy of living or happiness; God wants us to enjoy life, to have a good time. The second is in the context of worshiping God; we can experience joy in the presence of the Lord. Last and most difficult to sometimes understand is the joy that can be found through hardship.

## Read Ecclesiastes 9:7.

If you are like many adult children of dysfunctional families, you have a hard time enjoying life. This is a special problem for Christians because of a history of "Thou shalt nots" within the Christian culture. But enjoying life is included in God's plan. It helps break the compulsion cycle and cravings that keep you locked into addictions. Enjoying life helps you feel better about who you are as a child of God.

1. **What is the difference between happiness and joy?**

2. **Name five simple and easy things you can do every day to enjoy life (watch the stars at night, swing at a local park, take a walk, read a book).**

3. **What stops you from involving yourself in these activities on a daily basis?**

## Read Psalm 16:11.

1. **How can you find joy in the presence of God?**

2. **Are you involved in daily time with God through meditation and prayer? How can you work on this?**

3. **Are you involved in regular corporate worship? How can you work on this?**

4. How can worshiping with other believers help you overcome some of the rules that governed your dysfunctional family?

5. How can worshiping with other believers help you feel less isolated from God and other people?

6. How can the assurance of God's presence help you to trust God and other people?

## Read John 15:9–11.

1. How can you have joy in the midst of distress created by your adult-child issues?

2. How can Christ help you rise above your adversities?

3. Do you have a vital relationship with Jesus Christ?

Christ provides us with a new perspective on our lives. Joy comes when we experience the love and grace that Christ makes available to us. You can begin a relationship with Christ by simply asking. Tell God you wish to make right your relationship with him. Ask him to forgive the sins in your life. Invite Jesus Christ into your life to be your friend and counselor. If you have not done this, you can do so right now.

# RECOVERY GOALS

1. What will you do to begin overcoming the five rules that govern dysfunctional families?

2. What simple pleasure will you do on a daily basis?

3. Find a support group to attend regularly, whether that be an Adult Children of Alcoholics meeting, an Al-Anon group, or a church support group. What group will you attend?

4. Commit yourself to regular involvement in a church worship service. What service do you feel most comfortable actively attending?

# 4.　I Want to Feel Normal: Peace

## RECOVERY FOCUS

- Identify how denial has affected you.
- Name your issues.
- Find the peace of God.

## RECOVERY INFORMATION

Alcoholics Anonymous emphatically states that alcoholism is "cunning, baffling, and powerful." One of alcoholism's most powerful forces is that of denial. If you have attended Al-Anon groups, you have undoubtedly heard of the "pink elephant in the living room." The pink elephant represents the chaos and disruption caused by drinking. Wet-alcoholic families learn to tiptoe around this pink elephant, denying that it is a problem—or even denying its existence.

In the dry-alcoholic, the no-alcohol-alcoholic, and the no-alcohol-dysfunctional families, denial also operates. These dysfunctional families believe that all is well in their families even though something is wrong. They play a game of pretend in which they learn dysfunctional rules and believe them to be the norm.

If you grew up in an alcoholic family, you knew something was not quite right. However, you had learned not to trust your instincts, so you dismissed this feeling. As you grew older and gained more experience, as you met more people and learned about how they lived, and as you explored God's will for your life, that feeling you had dismissed returned. Something is awry in your life. Could it have something to do with the family system in which you were raised?

That gnawing feeling has led you into recovery. Perhaps you have explored other books, support groups, or therapy in your quest to figure out why things are not quite right in your life.

Some of you reading this book may not be Christians. We hope you continue working through this workbook and remain open-minded about the healing power of Christ available to you.

Those of you who are Christians have an additional barrier to break, a special form of denial. You may have believed that a relationship with Christ would right all the wrongs in your life. But soon you discovered that being a Christian was not enough to set you free from the confusion and pain of your past. In fact, hearing the judgmental, critical voices of some Christians, you feared rejection by God and by the church, so you buried even deeper the problems your upbringing created for you.

But those problems followed you into your adult years. You brought the roles and rules from your childhood family into your adult life, and your past has caught up with you. You have found that, in spite of all your reading of the Bible and praying, you have continued with self-defeating and self-destructive behaviors.

As difficult as it is to admit defeat in your life, you must. Doing so will in no way reflect negatively on your Christian beliefs, for your dysfunctional past cannot stand in the way of your salvation through Christ. Rather, admitting defeat allows you to give yourself over to God, asking for his help and grace as you confront your past. As you begin to talk with God, yourself, and others about your past and its impact on your life today, you will begin to experience the serenity and peace God intended for you.

## ISSUES RISE TO THE SURFACE

Perhaps, until recently, you were able to deny that anything was wrong in your life. Then you underwent a divorce, a loss of a job, a severe illness, or some other crisis, and you realized that something was amiss in your life. So you began to explore your past for clues.

When you experience a crisis or begin exploring your past, issues will rise to the surface. Slowly you will begin to break the "Don't-feel," "Don't-talk," and "Don't-feel-good-about-yourself" rules. You will feel overwhelmed with guilt, shame, and anger as you become aware of how your growing-up years adversely affected your adulthood. You will begin to think about things you repressed long ago. You will realize that you are worth more than you ever gave yourself credit for.

As you become aware of your dysfunctional past, you will also begin to remember more. Painful memories that you have until now repressed will begin to surface. Don't deny or repress those memories. In order for you to heal, you *must* recognize and acknowledge your past. If you can't take a good, hard look at your past, you are doomed to repeat its mistakes. You will either recover or repeat. And without focusing on what happened to you, you increase the likelihood of passing your dysfunction on to your children.

Reflect on the family tree you filled out in chapter 1. Your self-defeating behaviors have a long history. If you don't believe you will repeat the generational cycle, remember that the majority of adult children of alcoholics become alcoholics and drug addicts themselves. Many who don't become alcoholics or drug addicts develop other addictions like smoking, gambling, eating disorders, compulsive work habits, or religious compulsions. You need to examine your issues directly with God's help so that you can become more like Christ. The danger exists that even if you don't repeat the alcoholism of your parents and grandparents, you will continue with the *ism*, the self-defeating behavioral patterns that have afflicted your life.

You are not alone. If you are working through this book by yourself, you need to be reassured that your growing-up experiences were not unique. If you're working through this material in a group, you will hear elements of your story in the stories told by others.

As you gain insight into your dysfunctional childhood family, you will become aware of the issues that have created difficulties in your life. The following is a partial list of the issues affecting adult children. Check those issues that have affected your life.

- [ ] Rigidity
- [ ] Depression
- [ ] Panic attacks
- [ ] Perfectionism
- [ ] People pleasing
- [ ] Explosive anger
- [ ] Intimacy problems
- [ ] Suicidal thoughts
- [ ] Impulsive behavior
- [ ] Distrust of others
- [ ] Fear of abandonment
- [ ] All-or-none thinking
- [ ] Resistance to change
- [ ] Problems with honesty
- [ ] Avoidance of feelings
- [ ] High level of anxiety
- [ ] Approval-seeking behavior
- [ ] Addictions or compulsions

☐ Criticism of self and others
☐ Love of crisis and excitement
☐ Inappropriate sexual behavior
☐ Difficulty having healthy fun
☐ Difficulty completing projects
☐ Stress-related physical disorders
☐ Difficulty with those in authority
☐ Feelings of inadequacy, incompetency
☐ Over-responsibility or irresponsibility
☐ Highly manipulative and controlling behavior
☐ Negativity (seeing the worst in every situation)
☐ Sabotage of self in relationships and achievements
☐ Phobias (like fear of flying, heights, snakes, or crowds)

## RECOVERY PROBERS

1. How has alcoholism had a "cunning, baffling, and powerful" effect on your family? On your growing-up years? On your adult life?

2. When did you first begin to put your finger on the fact that something was not quite right with your life?

3. How have you let your Christianity feed your denial?

4. Have you found that you blocked out many childhood memories?

## RECOVERY GUIDE

But the fruit of the Spirit is . . . peace. (Galatians 5:22)

### Read Psalm 13:1–2.

1. How close are David's feelings to your own?

2. Describe the feelings you have been experiencing as you have reflected on growing up in a dysfunctional home.

3. Talk with God about these feelings, just as David did.

## Read Psalm 4:8 and 13:5–6.

1. How can you feel safe by trusting in God?

2. How difficult is it for you to place your trust in God in the midst of your pain?

## Read John 14:27.

1. What comfort does this verse give you as you face your troubling past?

2. How is God's peace different from the peace the world gives?

3. According to this verse, how do you receive God's peace?

## Read John 16:33.

1. What troubles have you had in this world because of your dysfunctional family system?

2. What does it mean to you personally that God has already overcome the world and its troubles?

## Read Romans 8:6 and Proverbs 3:5–6.

The Bible talks about peace *with* God and the peace *of* God. The first is the peace we can have with God through faith in Jesus Christ (Romans 5:1). We can be in a right relationship with God when our sins are forgiven. But this doesn't automatically give us the peace of God. For that we must surrender our lives to God. This can be a tough task for adult children of dysfunctional families. You have been hurt and abused. You often confuse God's love with judgment. Your distorted notions of trust and of God can hinder total surrender to his care.

1. What obstacles do you need to overcome before you can surrender or trust your life with all your issues to God?

2. What is the worst thing that could come from surrendering your life to God?

3. What is the best thing that could come from surrendering your life to God?

## Read Philippians 4:6–7.

1. What are the prerequisites to having the peace of God guard your heart and mind?

2. How is God's peace like a guard standing at the door of your heart and mind?

3. What specific anxieties must you surrender to God?

**Read 1 Thessalonians 5:23–24.**

1. How can God's peace penetrate your whole spirit, soul, and body?

2. How can God's peace bring you serenity and help break the patterns you've lived with in your dysfunctional home?

## RECOVERY GOALS

1. The prophet Isaiah affirms that God will keep in perfect peace the person whose mind is steadfast and who trusts in God (Isaiah 26:3). How can you rely on God as you work through your issues?

   .

2. Write down two or three ways you can commit your life to the Lord this next week.

3. Are you denying your anxious reactions or escalating your anxiety rather than turning this anxiety over to God?

4. When you feel your anxiety level on the rise, consider Philippians 4:6–7 and talk with God about this anxiety.

# 5.

# I Can't Take This Anymore: Patience

## RECOVERY FOCUS

- Discover how you *react* rather than *act* in responding to events and people.
- Examine how anxiety drives you to self-defeating behaviors.
- Learn to act purposefully, with patience rather than reactivity.

## RECOVERY INFORMATION

The enemy of patience is reactivity, behavior that reacts to external events and people without thinking or without considering the consequences. As an adult child of an alcoholic or other dysfunctional family, you often react to your circumstances with anger and frustration. Your reactions create pain for yourself and others. It's normal to feel frustrated when things don't go the way you want them to. However, you often have more difficulty with your reactivity and anxiety. It's here you need the patience only the Holy Spirit can give.

Patience helps you stand back and reflect on what you are doing. You can learn to *act* instead of *react*. Your reactivity to circumstances in your life is the hook that enmeshes you in other people's problems, that puts you in the victim role, that kicks in your perfectionism and impulsiveness. Patience counters this reactivity and allows more internal peace and purposeful action. Patience is being controlled by God's Spirit and resting in his goodness.

Even Moses had difficulty remaining patient. Numbers 20 tells us that when God told Moses to speak to the rock to bring forth water, Moses—feeling angry and frustrated—took his staff and struck the rock. God took Moses' reactivity as a lack of trust in him. And when you react to your circumstances rather than act purposefully, you too are not trusting enough in God.

Reactivity takes a variety of forms in the adult child of a dysfunctional family. Examine each of the following descriptions, deciding if any of them describe you.

## YOU WANT TO SOLVE OTHER PEOPLE'S PROBLEMS

You take care of others to the exclusion of your own needs. You feel better when you can reach out to others and comfort them. Because you are anxious about your own life, you also worry about the problems others have. This excessive worrying relieves your own anxiety but gets you overinvolved in the problems of others, leaving little time or energy for you to address your own problems.

This reaction is more than caregiving behavior. Caregiving is a compassionate reaching out to others in need *without* losing yourself in the process.

Where did this reaction originate? Growing up in a dysfunctional home, you were not adequately nurtured and cared for. Often the needs of your hurting parents came before yours. Now as an adult, you enmesh yourself in other people's lives in unhealthy ways to meet your unfulfilled needs. You give and give and give. And you have confused this with being selfless and serving God.

When you rescue others, you usually are responding to the anxiety you feel about a person's life. Your anxiety compulsively pushes you to fix their lives. Rescuing is a compulsive activity because you have to fix someone or their circumstances rather than being able to trust in God's sovereignty. Your rescuing acts as if God isn't there, or if he is, he's not able to intervene. Your motives are driven by anxiety, even though your intentions are good.

This is difficult for you to see, but patience can help you stand back and take an inventory of your motives. What you are doing might be right and good yet compulsive and destructive to your own well-being. You are reacting to the anxiety you feel instead of acting in the Spirit of God. You need to yield to God and his sovereignty. This is not to condemn what you do when you want to rescue others. You just need to stand back and reflect on the situation.

## YOU ACT LIKE A VICTIM

A second reaction adult children often fall into is playing the "poor-me" role. You get the attention of others by overdramatizing your situation. You feel sorry for yourself and pull others into your pity. You complain about your aches and pains, your home problems, and your financial affairs in order to get others involved in your life. You wallow in unhappiness. You exaggerate hurts or threats to make yourself the center of attention. You feel you have so much in life that you must endure. This is not patience.

You need to step back, gain perspective, and determine how out of proportion your thinking is. Ask yourself, How would other people view this situation? Blowing situations out of proportion is a relief valve for your anxiety. A healthier relief valve for your anxiety is getting a proper perspective on the situation.

## YOU ARE A PERFECTIONIST

When you were growing up, did you often feel that if only you could be perfect, then your parents would accept you? Did you suffer through parental rejection in spite of the fact you gave 110 percent of your effort? Have you set goals you can't possibly attain? Does your house have to be spotless? Are you so dedicated that you will work at your job until you drop?

You have suffered unnecessarily because of your need to be perfect. But perfectionism will not bring you satisfaction. Your accomplishments offer you little consolation. You still feel guilty and inadequate.

Patience comes from being able to be flexible and realistic in your expectations of life, yourself, and others rather than demanding perfection. Like your wanting to solve others' problems or playing the "poor-me" role, your perfectionism is driven by your anxiety.

## YOU ARE IMPULSIVE

Another reaction adult children of dysfunctional families often have is impulsive behavior. You do things before you consider the consequences. You have an urgent need that must be met—now. You tend to rush into decisions before thinking them through. You lock yourself into one direction and can't see any alternatives.

This impulsive behavior often forces your life into a crisis mode. You don't start out wanting crises; they just seem to follow you around. Your impulsiveness creates one crisis after another. And you end up feeling miserable as you clean up the messes you have created. Your impulsive business decisions often end in disaster. This is classic alcoholic thinking. Just as alcoholics get urges to drink and can't get them out of their minds, you get an idea and want to act on it immediately. This explains why adult children suffer from an abundance of compulsions.

## INSANITY

Did you find yourself in those descriptions? You may feel you have suffered long over these issues. They have tripped you up, but you've gotten right back up and practiced them again.

Alcoholics Anonymous popularized the saying, "Insanity is doing the same thing over and over and over again, expecting different results." Is this what has happened to you? You expected that if you kept trying these things again and again, you would feel some serenity in your life. But you feel as anxious as ever. You react with the same behavioral responses that you learned in childhood. And you are doing them over and over and over again, still suffering, but not achieving new results. Patiently enduring your self-defeating behaviors is not peace. It's insanity.

Patience is rising above your circumstances to face your issues. When you were growing up, you did the best you could. After all, you didn't have too many choices. But as an adult, you do. You don't need to continue in your self-defeating behaviors. As an adult you can now learn to rise above difficult circumstances. You can be an actor in life rather than a reactor. This is the essence of patience.

## RECOVERY PROBERS

1. How has reactivity hooked you into rescuing others, playing the victim, perfectionism, or impulsiveness?

2. In what ways do you rescue or take care of other people to the exclusion of your own needs?

3. How do you act like a victim?

4. In what ways do you act impulsively?


5. How reactive are you when you feel anxious?


6. How can you patiently stand back and reflect with God on situations rather than react?


## RECOVERY GUIDE

But the fruit of the Spirit is . . . patience. (Galatians 5:22)

### Read Luke 10:40.

Martha reacted to the anxiety she felt performing her duties. In her caregiving role she had taken on too much responsibility. She was over-functioning. Thinking that her service to others was the good and proper thing to be doing, she became angry with Jesus. The Lord pointed out that her worry and anxiety had taken her focus off what was important in life.

1. How does being anxious contribute to your overlooking your own limits?


2. How are you like Martha, feeling overly responsible for others?


3. How can you use more patience to reflect with God on what really needs to happen when you begin reacting to your anxiety?

**Read Jonah 4:8.**

Jonah here played the role of the victim. He reacted to his anxiety by under-functioning. He wanted God to feel sorry for him. God pointed out to him that rather than blame and pity, he should attend to his responsibilities. God was asking that Jonah reflect on his circumstances, take responsibility for what he could, and leave the rest to God.

1. In what ways are you like Jonah?

2. In what ways could you take responsibility for what is yours to take and trust God for what is out of your control?

**Read Colossians 1:11–12.**

1. According to these verses, what is the source of patience?

2. How can you draw more on God's power to act rather than react to those around you?

3. How can you respect your limits and draw from God's limitless power?

## RECOVERY GOALS

1. Describe a recent situation in which you reacted by rescuing someone.

2. Reflect on that situation and list three alternative, healthy ways you could have responded.

3. Describe a recent situation in which you reacted by playing the victim.

4. Reflect on that situation and list three alternative, healthy ways you could have responded.

5. Describe a recent situation in which you reacted by becoming perfectionistic.

6. Reflect on that situation and list three alternative, healthy ways you could have responded.

7. Describe a recent situation in which you reacted with impulsive behavior.

8. Reflect on that situation and list three alternative, healthy ways you could have responded.

9. The next time you catch yourself reacting to a situation rather than purposefully acting, stop, reflect, and think through some options. When you do this, you are less likely to react in a self-defeating manner.

# 6.

# I'll Give You Something to Cry About: Kindness

## RECOVERY FOCUS

- Learn why you have difficulty showing kindness.
- Understand how you overidentify or underidentify with others.
- Learn a method for expressing honesty that will promote kindness.

## RECOVERY INFORMATION

You may remember as a kid saying, "When I grow up, I'm never going to do to my kids what my parents have done to me." This is a negative version of the golden rule. You decided that you would not do to others what was done to you. In spite of the fact that you vowed never to treat your kids or others the way you yourself were treated, you have and often still do!

One of the reasons this happens to adult children of alcoholic or other dysfunctional families is that they lack empathy for others. When as a child you felt sad or hurt, your parents expressed little empathy toward you. You were told to "just get over it." When you cried, you were called a baby or were spanked. Or your parents shamed you by saying things like, "I'll give you something to cry about."

In functional families, parents attempt to understand and validate their children's perspective. This gives their children permission to be comfortable with their own feelings. When children feel lonely or hurt, parents in functional families respond with empathic kindness, teaching their children to better handle the circumstances they face.

Your sadness probably was not met by an empathic response but by rigidity and anger. Your parents had difficulty seeing life as you saw it. It was tough for your parents to allow you to have feelings different from theirs. This again is the "Don't-feel" message. You grew up in a family where you were there for the benefit of your parents. In short, your parents could not empathize with you. So you have difficulty appropriately expressing empathy and validating the way others feel. And without empathy, it's tough for you to show kindness.

## OVERIDENTIFICATION

Chris found herself absorbed in Liz's problems. Chris thought her rescuing behaviors were an indication of her Christian compassion. As she became absorbed in someone else's problems, they became her problems as well. When Liz's husband filed for divorce, Chris was there for her, but Chris's own family suffered. Her marriage deteriorated. She was so concerned about Liz that her own life was put on hold. It was as if Chris didn't know where she ended and other people began.

Chris's father had been mean and angry, and Chris's mother made it up to the children by being overprotective of their feelings. Chris had identified with the codependency of her mother and now felt responsible for everybody's bad feelings. She was on a crusade to make bad feelings go away.

Maybe you are like Chris. In varying degrees you become so emotionally entangled in the problems of others that you lose a strong sense of your own identity. You confuse pity with empathy and rescue those in need. Yet what they need most is your objective empathy. Instead they get smothered by your overinvolvement.

## UNDERIDENTIFICATION

Kyle came home after work tired. He was expecting a quiet evening, maybe some television and a walk. His son met him at the door, anxious and upset, needing help with his homework. Kyle snapped at him, which only made his son withdraw to his bedroom. Kyle couldn't understand why his twelve-year-old demanded his help. What Kyle didn't understand and appreciate was the fact that his son also had had a bad day.

Kyle was unable to be empathic, to put himself in his son's shoes. And because of this lack of perspective, Kyle was not kind to his son.

Growing up in a dysfunctional home, Kyle learned the "Don't-feel" lesson well. Kyle's father was a good man, the stable member of his family. His mother was a very hysterical woman and very unstable. Kyle's dad's philosophy was "be strong," which meant ignore your feelings and do what needs to be done.

No wonder Kyle couldn't identify with his son's feelings. Kyle's inability to feel his own hurts and brokenness or identify with those of other people made him highly critical of others. He judged others—and himself—without mercy. Kyle's lack of empathy left him without the ability to accept others' feelings. His wife, Anita, saw him as cold and distant.

Maybe you are like Kyle. Your lack of empathy keeps you uninvolved in the lives of others. Intimacy is nearly impossible when you lack the ability to express kindness.

## KINDNESS OUT OF EMPATHY

If you are like many people, your father most likely underidentified with you, while your mother overidentified with you. In your treatment of people, you often fluctuate between the two extremes. But neither overidentification nor underidentification is a healthy expression of kindness.

Kenneth Haugk, in his book *Christian Caregiving: A Way of Life,* states that Christian empathy contains a solid measure of objectivity. It is this objectivity that allows the Christian to demonstrate a compassionate kindness. When you can identify with other people's problems without losing yourself in them, you are capable of compassionately responding with kindness rather than rescuing with pity.

Chris needs to learn to identify more objectively with the problems her family and friends experience. When you overidentify, you are protecting others to the exclusion of yourself and your own needs. You need to begin practicing letting go of the pain of others while still caring. You need to remember that empathy doesn't eliminate the pain others feel. You can learn to take the perspective of others without losing your own perspective in the process.

Kyle needs to learn to consider his own feelings as well as the feelings of his family and friends. When you underidentify with others, it's usually because you are out of touch with your own feelings. This served to protect you in the past but is wearing thin in your present relationships. Yet you don't feel safe enough to share your feelings. In your growing-up years, there was no payoff for sharing your feelings. You need to take risks and be vulnerable in at least beginning to share how you feel. You need to begin experimenting with being honest with your own feelings. As you do this, you'll find yourself being empathic with the feelings and situations of others.

## COMMUNICATE EFFECTIVELY

What you need in your relationships is a dose of honesty. When you honestly share how you feel, you are more likely to take responsibility for your own feelings and behaviors. This counteracts both your inclinations to overidentify and underidentify with others.

You can best do this by sending "I messages" rather than "you messages" to others. The concept of the "I message" was first introduced by Dr. Thomas Gordon, the founder of the Parent Effectiveness Training movement. "I messages" have been incorporated into many of today's popular parenting and relationship approaches.

Most adult children of alcoholic or other dysfunctional families send only "you messages" when they have a problem with someone:

"You make me so mad."

"You treat me just awful."

"You can do better than that."

"You messages" communicate a one-up, one-down message that tells others what they should do, how they ought to live, what they should think. "You messages" engage others in power struggles, encourage codependent relationships, and generally shame and blame. When you send a "you message," you communicate that you have the solution to the problems others have. "You messages" allow you to put the blame outside of yourself. When you send a "you message," you discount what others are feeling and impose your will on theirs.

"I messages," on the other hand, help you communicate what you are feeling without taking on the feelings and the problems of another. "I messages," are less likely to be met with resistance. An "I message" consists of three important but simple parts:

I feel [state honestly how you feel],

when you [state the other's behavior]

because [state why].

Kyle could have given his son the following "I message": "I feel annoyed when you ask me to help as soon as I walk in the door because I'm so tired after working all day. Please give me thirty minutes of time by myself." By simply sending this "I message," Kyle could have shown kindness to his son.

Chris would have benefited from sending "I messages" because she would have been able to retain her objectivity in relating to Liz.

Instead, she became absorbed in Liz's problems by giving advice, directing, diagnosing, and sympathizing. Chris could have said: "I feel sad when I hear you talk about your marital problems because I know you really do want things to work out with your husband." This empathic message would have communicated her kindness without overidentifying with Liz's plight.

## RECOVERY PROBERS

1. How empathic were your parents with you?


2. Are you more like Chris or Kyle?


3. How do you become emotionally entangled with others?


4. How does your lack of empathy keep you from showing kindness to others?


5. How can you retain your objectivity when you show kindness to others?


6. How can "I messages" help you empathize and show kindness?


## RECOVERY GUIDE

But the fruit of the Spirit is . . . kindness. (Galatians 5:22)

### Read Luke 10:30.

The story of the Good Samaritan is a practical illustration of kindness. Overidentifiers would have difficulty appropriately handling this type of situation. The man's wounds and desperate circumstances would heighten their anxiety and hook them into pitying and rescuing behavior. They would, with tunnel vision, focus all their energy in saving this hurting man.

1. **Describe a relationship where you rescued out of pity and found yourself in an unhealthy situation.**

2. **What has been the outcome of this relationship?**

## Read Luke 10:31–32.

The priest and Levite were examples of underidentifiers. They lacked the objective empathy necessary to express kindness. They were unable to identify with this poor man's condition.

1. **Describe a relationship in which you underidentify with the other person's situation.**

2. **What has been the outcome of this relationship?**

## Read Luke 10:33–35.

The Samaritan demonstrated kindness and caring. This expression grew out of an objective empathy that allowed the Samaritan to help the man while retaining his own identity. The Samaritan continued about his business! As an overidentifier, you would lean toward making the man your new business. You can learn from the Good Samaritan. This person was able to care in a way that did not consume. The objectivity of the Good Samaritan kept him from pitying. This is the kindness of which the Bible speaks.

**Read John 11:33.**

Jesus demonstrated kindness out of an objective empathy when he raised Lazarus from the dead. He was deeply grieved over Lazarus's death. Some wondered why he did not prevent the death (John 11:37). But Jesus didn't rescue Lazarus before death. He didn't overidentify or underidentify with Lazarus.

1. **Describe one way you could become more objective in your demonstration of empathy.**

2. **Name several people who could benefit from an objective demonstration of your empathy.**

## RECOVERY GOALS

1. **Recall three "you messages" you have sent recently. Write them down.**
   - 
   - 
   - 

2. **Rewrite each statement, using "I messages" instead of "you messages."**

   - I feel
     when you
     because

   - I feel
     when you
     because

   - I feel
     when you
     because

3. **Every day intentionally send one "I message" instead of a "you message."**

# 7.

# When I Take Care of Myself, I Feel Guilty: Goodness

## RECOVERY FOCUS

- Discover how dysfunctional-family rules can interfere with your recovery.
- Learn recovery tips that can guide your present recovery decisions.

## RECOVERY INFORMATION

You may feel overwhelmed as you begin to examine and address your issues. When you realize that the way you have been living your life has been counterproductive, you feel discouraged, defeated, and depressed. You grieve over the lost time, opportunities, and possibilities. You feel as if your childhood experiences set you up for failure as adults. You want to change, but change is scary.

The dysfunctional-family rules examined in chapter 3 can keep you from experiencing the serenity and recovery God desires for you. "Don't talk about real issues" pushes you to talk around your issues with others rather than getting directly to them. "Don't feel" keeps your feelings cut off. You find yourself reacting to the painful emotions that bubble up rather than validating and talking about them.

The "Don't-trust" rule makes it difficult to seek the help you so earnestly desire. You are afraid that others may learn about the real you and not like what they see. And that is scary! You may not be accepted for who you are or for what you have done. And acceptance is what you crave and need. The "Don't-get-too-close" rule piggybacks on the "Don't-trust" rule in keeping you from getting support from others.

You want to recover all by yourself. But this is wishful thinking. You need other people.

"Don't feel good about yourself" keeps you beating up on yourself. Taking care of yourself makes you feel guilty. You feel that you do not deserve better. Growing up, you thought the family chaos was somehow your fault.

You believe that Christians are supposed to take care of others and not worry about themselves. But you need to take care of yourself for God to be able to use you. Taking care of yourself is not selfish; it's essential to living the Christian life fully. You need to be good to yourself. And you can do this while keeping God number one in your life.

## A RECOVERY PROGRAM

We recommend that you become part of a twelve-step recovery program such as Al-Anon, Codependents Anonymous, or Adult Children of Alcoholics. Working through the Twelve Steps can help you experience God's grace and maintain your emotional sobriety. As we said before, find a group that is soundly based on Scripture. If such a group is not available in your area, you will benefit greatly from studying *The Twelve Steps for Christians from Addictive and Other Dysfunctional Families* (Recovery Publications).

## SOME RECOVERY TIPS

*Go slowly*. You'll need time to recover. The process is painful and can't be rushed. Your impulsiveness, perfectionism, and black-or-white thinking may urge you to speed up the recovery process. Joan wanted desperately to feel better, "to be like everyone else," as she said. Once she realized her self-defeating behaviors, thoughts, and attitudes were a result of growing up with an alcoholic father, she called her two sisters and told them of her insights. She was surprised that the two of them didn't appreciate her new understanding of their growing-up experiences. She discussed her life story with a co-worker, who spread rumors about her past. Joan's motivation was good, but in her rush for recovery, she moved too fast.

*Ask for help*. As adult children, you have learned that it's best to solve your problems by yourself. The "Don't-trust" rule keeps you from believing that others can help you. You alienate and isolate yourself from others, expecting from them the worst judgmental attitudes and actions. You need to learn to reach out to others who are trustworthy and ask for their assistance. This help can come from a therapist, a support group, a pastor, or trusted friend. We again encourage you to attend an Al-Anon or an Adult Children of Alcoholics support group. Enlisting the help of a therapist trained in the alcoholism field can be valuable. Reading books about alcoholism and adult-children issues will give you insightful information that can aid in the recovery process.

*Avoid blaming.* You can easily get stuck in your recovery by blaming your problems on your parents. This Recovery Discovery workbook was not intended as an excuse for you to blame your parents, a stepparent, or guardians for your circumstances. Whether they did or didn't do the best they could in raising you, their problems are not yours. You need to lay aside blame. No good can come from pointing the finger at an alcoholic father, a physically abusive mother, a mentally ill stepfather. This doesn't mean you continue to deny the pain and loss you experienced growing up. Acknowledge what has happened, then choose to move on with your life rather than build up resentments and rage about your past. Focus on present change rather than past blame.

*Recognize you can't fix your parents (or siblings).* You may want to rescue your parents from their alcoholic or dysfunctional patterns of living. You need to remember that rescuing is one of your issues. You can't make your parents better, no matter how much you try. The conditions in which you grew up were not your fault. The condition in which your parents find themselves today is also not your fault. Your job is not to fix your parents (or siblings) but to pray for them. You may explore a professional intervention for your parents with a qualified therapist. We recommend that adult children not make any quick decision regarding how to handle their parents (and siblings). This needs to be a careful, prayerful decision that takes time, wisdom from others, and information.

*Have some fun.* Given the rigid roles and rules under which you grew up, it's no surprise that you have difficulty relaxing. Enjoying life is part of recovery. You didn't get much of a chance to be a kid. Managing the chaos of growing up ate up much of your energy. Today, life is much the same. You expend most of your energy in simply getting through the week. There is not much left for you to enjoy. You need to make an effort to carve out time for fun and relaxation.

*Deepen your walk with God.* Spending time in quiet reflection, prayer, and Bible reading is helpful. You can't recover using your own resources. Spend time with other Christians, talking, sharing, worshiping. Find Christians who will not be judgmental, who will walk with you in your recovery.

*Work at an ongoing program of recovery.* You need to take steps to avoid relapsing into your old patterns of relating to yourself, God, and others. Your devotional life and worship at church can partly fulfill this need. However, you need to remain vigilant in your working of the Twelve Steps in order to stay in touch with your issues and God's will for your life. Many adult children identify their self-defeating attitudes and behaviors, gain some relief from their anxiety and pain, and believe they are somehow cured. Then they move on with their lives, failing to continue their recovery program. In time they find themselves falling back into their old ways. Consider a continued involvement in a twelve-step recovery program.

## RECOVERY PROBERS

1. How do you feel the dysfunctional-family rules you learned could interfere with your recovery?



2. How can you take the time to take care of your recovery without becoming self-centered?



3. What is the biggest obstacle to involving yourself in a twelve-step program of recovery?



4. How can you pace your recovery so as not to rush God's healing in your life?



5. What is the most appropriate help you need to seek at this time (further reading, a support group, counseling)?

6. How does blaming your parents interfere with your recovery?

7. How will you handle your relationship with your parents (whether or not your parents are still living)?

8. How can you take yourself a little less seriously and have fun?

## RECOVERY GUIDE

But the fruit of the Spirit is . . . goodness. (Galatians 5:22)

### Read Ephesians 3:16–19.

Foundational to your recovery is God's goodness. You can't be good to yourself without the recognition that you serve a good and gracious God. One way of recognizing God's goodness is through a gratitude list.

1. List ten ways God has been good to you:
   - 
   - 
   - 
   - 
   - 
   - 
   - 
   - 
   - 
   - 

2. How can you "grasp" in an experiential way the infinite quality of God's love for you?

**Read Hebrews 4:15 and Isaiah 53:3–6.**

God is not aloof and distant. He cared so much for you that he became flesh and blood and lived among humans. Through Jesus Christ, God experienced humanity. He can empathize with your life conditions, your pain, and your joys because he too experienced them in a human way.

1. **What self-defeating attitudes and behaviors have you felt God could not relate to?**

2. **As you reflect on the humanity of God through Jesus Christ, how do you feel God can relate to these self-defeating attitudes and behaviors?**

3. **How does this realization help you surrender your hurts, behaviors, and attitudes to Christ?**

**Read Hebrews 4:16.**

1. **What courage and comfort does this verse give you?**

2. **In what areas of recovery do you need the most help from God?**

**Read Psalm 34.**

This psalm describes God's providence and goodness toward you. Verse 6 describes adult children, those who are ill-equipped to live the

Christian life. God, however, is equipped and can deliver you. As you recognize God's goodness and your dependence on him, God can work in you.

**1. How are you ill-equipped to handle your own recovery?**

**2. How is God equipped to help with your recovery?**

## RECOVERY GOALS

**1. Committing to an ongoing program of recovery can seem overwhelming. This is why adult children who are working a program of recovery find it useful to talk about recovering "one day at a time." Say the following statements aloud:**
  • One day at a time I can commit to work a program of recovery.
  • One day at a time I can surrender my life to God.
  • One day at a time I can be good to myself.
  • One day at a time I can treat others differently.
  • One day at a time I can experience God's goodness in my life.

**2. Complete the following sentences to help you to commit to recovery one day at a time.**
  • Today, I will work a program of recovery that . . .

  • Today, I will ask God to . . .

  • Today, I will seek to . . .

# 8.

# I'm Afraid of Getting Too Close: Faithfulness

## RECOVERY FOCUS

- Examine your issues with intimacy.
- Learn the four components of active communication.
- Understand how your intimacy issues affect your relationship to God.

## RECOVERY INFORMATION

Growing up in an alcoholic or other dysfunctional family, you didn't see many models of loving relationships. You remember your parents fighting and know that isn't what you want. You recall your parents' marriage and vow not to repeat their mistakes. You know you want more out of your relationships, but you're not sure how to make that happen. You know what you don't want, but you've never had a realistic view of what you need or how to have those needs met.

In your childhood home you experienced your parents' harsh discipline rather than their empathic acceptance. Your parents inconsistently expressed their love to each other and to you.

All of this has tainted and confused your expectations of what constitutes an intimate and faithful relationship. You don't have much experience in getting close to others in healthy ways.

Many adult children of dysfunctional families have trouble with intimacy. Several issues may block your intimacy with your spouse or your friends or your dating partner, and even God. Let's examine some of the intimacy issues you may be facing.

## YOU DON'T KNOW HOW TO GET CLOSE

If your childhood family was governed by dysfunctional-family rules, you had a hard time making personal relationships within the family. Closeness was never valued. This meant you also never learned the basic social skills necessary to develop healthy relationships with others. You simply don't know how to get close.

## IT'S US AGAINST THE WORLD

Somehow your family was different from other people's families, and in a strange way you stuck together to face any foe that challenged your family system. You were told it's "us against the world." But this mentality didn't work. Your parents didn't always support you emotionally. This left you isolated in a hurting family, and it has left you isolated today. This is one reason why so many adult children feel so different around other people.

Alienation—feeling different, disconnected, and estranged—is very much a part of the adult-child experience. This limits your healthy friendships. You tend to isolate from others, preferring to remain alone or with only a few people. Intimate relationships are especially troublesome and plagued with problems. Your family relationships did not teach you how to work through feelings of alienation, so you naturally distanced and isolated. You felt frustrated and blamed others for how you felt. The "us-against-the-world" mentality also operated *within* your family to produce an "us-against-them" mentality toward each other. You didn't trust each other, and you didn't work toward building broken relationships.

## YOU'RE AFRAID TO SHOW THE REAL YOU

At first glance many adult children appear to have it all together. You are good at "looking good." But deep inside you know that you aren't as together as you seem. You feel you must be better than you really are to be accepted. You're afraid that if people knew the real you, they wouldn't want to love you. You have many façades and are afraid to be genuine for fear of rejection or loss of false pride. Deception rather than honesty and humility reigned in your family.

You come off as a know-it-all, when in fact you wish you knew so much more. One way you learned not to show the real you in your family was through keeping secrets. You protected your dysfunctional family by playing a psychological game of hide-and-seek. You hid the fact that your mom was an alcoholic or that your dad sexually abused you or that your stepmother was crazy. If you closely examine your family, you will find many skeletons in the closets. You felt if you were really honest, you would be disloyal or unfaithful. So you never really developed a healthy faithfulness in your family relationships. You hid your feelings, thoughts, and behavior. And you continue to live with these secrets. You're still afraid that if people knew your secrets, they wouldn't love you.

## YOU NEED OTHERS' APPROVAL TO FEEL GOOD ABOUT YOURSELF

You grew up with parents who were limited in their ability to meet your needs, validate your feelings, encourage your growth and independence. You were emotionally, spiritually, and sometimes physically abandoned. This did not allow you the opportunity to develop a healthy sense of yourself. In the absence of this kind of loving support, you grew up dependent on what others thought of you. This has left you with a fear of being abandoned. The "Don't-feel-good-about-yourself" rule keeps you relying on others to feel good about yourself. So you try your hardest to please others. You feel lonely and hurt since you can't always please everyone.

Janet feels as if she walks on eggshells at work. She wonders if she is saying the right thing, dressing appropriately, even sitting right. During office meetings she feels she has little to contribute. She usually lets others talk first to see if what she is thinking is accurate. When things go well, she takes pride in what she does. But when she faces deadlines and other pressures, she feels lost and lonely. She is dependent on her co-workers to feel good about herself. If she were more secure and relaxed, she wouldn't need the constant support of those around her to feel good about herself. She could work more independently. She could also face herself honestly and humbly and gain support from God and herself.

## OTHER PEOPLE SHOULD BE ABLE TO READ YOUR MIND

You expect those close to you to know your needs automatically. You have a distorted view of what it means to be vulnerable and share needs, hurts, wants, and desires with others. You're afraid to be vulnerable. So you set up a fantasy of an intimate, caring relationship. You believe, unrealistically, that those who care about you will know your needs because they care about you. You focus more on who others "should be" and not on who they actually are.

## OTHER PEOPLE WILL MEET ALL (OR NONE) OF YOUR NEEDS

You often see your relationships in one of two ways: either you feel you must do all of the work, or you must do none of the work in a relationship. You set your expectations too high or too low. When you set high expectations for others, you set the relationship up to fail. You are being irresponsible when you believe that others are responsible for making your relationships work. Your high and usually unfulfilled expectations lead to the buildup of resentments, which leads to a lack of trust, alienation, and isolation. JoAnne expected her husband always to be there for her, never to be critical, never to tire of her demands. Her husband, Brian, waited on her hand and foot, but this was not enough. She grew resentful that he didn't make more money. They couldn't afford the car she wanted or take the sort of vacations she thought appropriate. Brian worked harder to get close to her by doing what she wanted. The more he tried to get close to her, the more JoAnne pushed him away. Their relationship had no reciprocity.

When you set your expectations too low, you find yourself carrying your relationships. You do all the work to make them successful. Brian is an example of an adult child who felt he was responsible for the success of the relationship. He over-functioned, believing that his actions toward JoAnne would win her approval.

Healthy relationships involve give and take. Adult children lean toward give relationships (and find people who will take and take) or take relationships (and find people who will give and give).

## CLOSENESS THROUGH COMMUNICATION

You can get closer to people by learning active communication skills. Good active communication allows closeness to build in two ways: you understand others better, and you share your life with others so that they understand you better. Active communication can begin the process of overcoming your intimacy issues. If you have not taken a class or been involved in a group that facilitates the development of communication skills, we encourage you to find one.

One of the mistakes made in communication is not taking seriously what the other person says. Responses like, "You don't feel that bad!" or "You don't really mean that" only invalidate the person's thoughts and feelings, cutting off the opportunity to build closeness and trust.

Active communication, however, helps you to validate the thoughts and feelings of others. When you actively communicate with others, you begin to grow in your relationship with them. Active communication consists of four basic components: focused attention, reflective listening, non-judgmental acceptance, and responsive sharing.

*Focused attention.* When you listen, you need to focus on what the person is saying, not on how you are going to respond to the person. Notice the person's body language and tone of voice. Listen beyond the words to the feelings. "What is Mary really feeling?" "Why might she be biting her lip?" "What point is she trying to make with me?"

*Reflective listening.* Reflective listeners not only listen attentively but also restate or reflect what they understand the other person to have said. This doesn't mean that you restate every thought the other person expresses but that you periodically check out with the person how you think he or she might be feeling. For example, Mary says, "You're spending too much time at work. You need to be home more." Careless listening might respond by saying, "You don't need to feel that way, Mary." Reflective listening would reflect to Mary the feeling you thought she was experiencing, "Mary, you seem angry or frustrated with me." This validates Mary's feelings. If Mary *isn't* angry or frustrated, then a reflective statement gives her the chance to help you clarify what she is feeling. She may say, "I'm not angry, I'm hurt." The relationship grows closer because you understand Mary better.

*Non-judgmental acceptance.* Christians are called to bear one another's burdens (Galatians 6:2). God is the God of redemption. He has called you to participate in his divine plan of reconciliation by loving, caring, praying for, and forgiving each other.

*Responsive sharing.* Active communication is more than actively listening. You need to respond by sharing your experiences as well. This creates a give-and-take communication, drawing you closer as you have the courage to disclose your life as well. But when you share your experiences, be careful not to interrupt, and do not get drawn into the game of one-upmanship.

## RECOVERY PROBERS

1. **What did you learn about intimate relationships while growing up?**

2. What relationship skills do you feel you need to learn more about to improve your relationships?

3. How do you find yourself feeling isolated from others? Is it from fear? Do you get angry and then feel alienated?

4. What is your biggest fear in sharing the real you with those close to you?

5. How has the "Don't-feel-good-about-yourself" rule affected your close relationships?

6. In what ways do you expect those close to you to read your mind?

7. Do you find yourself setting your expectations of other people too high or too low? How does this interfere with your intimacy with others?

8. How could active communication overcome your issues with intimacy?

## RECOVERY GUIDE

> But the fruit of the Spirit is . . . faithfulness. (Galatians 5:22)

### Read Proverbs 20:6.

1. **How have people failed you in ways that hinder your ability to become close?**

2. **How have your parents acted in ways that hinder your ability to become close?**

3. **How can you allow God's power and grace to help you work toward honesty, trust, humility, openness, acceptance, vulnerability, and forgiveness in those relationships?**

4. **What characteristics do you most need to focus on in your intimate relationships so that they can grow and mature?**

### Read 1 Corinthians 1:9.

God declares to you that he is faithful. And this faithful God has broken down the sin barrier that separated you from him. He wants your fellowship, your friendship. You are often not faithful in relationships; you break your promises, isolate yourself, keep secrets, lie, disrespect others, lack understanding and acceptance of others, and demonstrate a lack of trust. God, on the other hand, keeps his promises, seeks you out, is open and honest, respects you for who you are, is understanding and forgiving, and wants your trust.

1. **How have your adult-child issues with intimacy affected your present relationship with God?**

2. How does God's faithfulness help you to become more faithful in your relationships?

Read Romans 8:38–39.

1. When have you felt abandoned or alienated by God or other people?

2. How have these feelings of abandonment kept you from getting close to God or other people?

3. How does this passage speak to your feelings of abandonment?

4. How does knowing that God will never abandon you give you comfort and courage to work toward intimacy in your relationships?

5. How do your feelings of abandonment affect your accepting God's love and forgiveness?

6. How can you show more willingness to accept God's love?

**Read 1 John 1:9.**

1. Have you ever felt as if God would not forgive you?

2. Do you consistently ask God for forgiveness when you sin? Why or why not?

3. How does knowing that God forgives you help you move toward closeness in your relationships?

**Read 1 John 4:10–11.**

1. How does God's infinite love for you empower you to love other people?

2. How does God's love give you courage to gain closeness in your relationships?

## RECOVERY GOALS

You can begin practicing active communication right now. Choose a relationship in which you wish you could feel more closeness. Write next to the four components of active listening ways you can implement each of these components in these relationships.

1. **In my relationship to ___, I can practice active communication in these ways:**

Focused attention:

Reflective listening:

Non-judgmental acceptance:

Responsive sharing:

# 9.    I'm Not Mad: Gentleness

## RECOVERY FOCUS

- Learn what robs you of gentleness in your relationships.
- Discover what feelings are behind your anger.
- Examine how reflection on your anger can contribute to gentleness.

## RECOVERY INFORMATION

Was gentleness a part of your family? Probably not. Most alcoholic and dysfunctional homes are marked more by explosive anger than by gentleness. The inconsistency and unpredictability of someone reacting in anger combined with a high level of anxiety in your family made it nearly impossible for gentleness to permeate your home.

You probably grew up surrounded by conflict and volatile anger. You may have witnessed and experienced verbal abuse or physical violence or both.

If you were like most children, anger scared you. You saw your dad enraged at your mom. You watched as your mom verbally beat up your dad. Today you are afraid of angry people and afraid of your own anger. Just as you walked on eggshells around your parents' anger, you tiptoe around other people's anger and your own rage. You have trouble handling anger in appropriate ways. Just as your parents used anger to get what they wanted, you often use your anger to manipulate situations. You become demanding and verbally attack those around you. Or you stuff your anger, turning it into resentments, bitterness, or self-deprecation.

### FEAR AND INSECURITY

Behind your anger (whether you explode with it or stuff it) lies a scared little girl or little boy who was encouraged to hide hurts and fears. And those hurts and fears are with you today. The insecurity fostered in your dysfunctional home fuels your present anger.

Brenda remembers how her mother would become hysterical. "One Saturday afternoon, when I came home later than I had expected, my mom hit the ceiling. She went on and on about my friends being a bad influence on me, especially Mary. Later that day she asked if Mary was still coming over for dinner. It was as if she forgot all about her earlier outburst." The unpredictability of her mother's explosions left Brenda fearful and insecure. She never knew if her mother would love her or hate her.

Don recalls his father's violent outbursts. "When my dad walked by me, I instinctively ducked, not sure whether or not he was going to hit me." Don tries to joke about it, but the look on his face as he tells the story reveals the fear and insecurity he felt as the result of his father's behavior.

This fear and insecurity follow you into adult life in the form of anger. If you could scratch away your anger, you would find underneath it the fear and insecurity you felt as a child in a dysfunctional home. When you are fearful and insecure in a relationship, your anger is engaged. You build up resentments and bitterness. Your temper flares. Or you are passive-aggressive with your anger, getting revenge through procrastination or neglect.

When Brenda was a young girl, she felt an urgency to get her needs met. She had to approach her mother at the right moment to get the love and security she felt she needed. Now as an adult, when Brenda wants love and attention from her husband and doesn't get it right away, she becomes angry and demanding. She puts him down in front of his friends. She verbally attacks him. Her anger prompted by her insecurity serves only to push her husband further away emotionally.

## ATTENTION AND LOVE

Another roadblock to gentleness was the way your family expressed love. In dysfunctional families love is rarely gentle. Instead, people tend to be negative, focusing on what you do wrong rather than validating what you do well. The effort you put into tasks or relationships is rarely acknowledged. Love is not enjoyable.

The attention you were given was often negative. For example, you heard things like, "You're always making a mess. Clean up, you slob." Or you tried to get your parents' attention while they watched television, only to hear grunts and groans. Sometimes you were the scapegoat when you heard messages like, "I'm sick of you!"

This negative love and attention expressed in your family often came across to you as blame, criticism, or judgment. This was most evident in the way you were disciplined. Discipline in dysfunctional families often involves the withdrawal of love by the parent. And with this withdrawal of love came the message that your parents were angry with you. Their fears and insecurities were behind this anger, but you saw only the anger.

Healthy families express love and attention in positive ways. They acknowledge the efforts of family members, viewing them as important, no matter what they do. They express affirmation in comments like, "The yard really looks good after all the work you put into it," or "I love you!"

Part of recovery is becoming more positive and affirming in the way you love others as well as becoming more accepting of the positive affirmations others give you. It takes practice to change these patterns.

## RECOGNIZING FEELINGS BEHIND ANGER

You can learn to recognize and acknowledge the feelings that fuel your rage. And in so doing, you can choose responses other than anger. As an adult child, you probably get angry too easily. The rage you vent at yourself and others covers up your fears and insecurities as well as your inability to express and receive positive love and attention.

The next time you become angry, reflect on what feeling is fueling that anger. Do you feel hurt, embarrassed, unloved, guilty? Most often you will be able to identify a feeling that is contributing to your anger. Once you can name this other feeling, you can then choose to express this feeling rather than react to a situation or relationship in anger.

## RECOVERY PROBERS

1. **How consistently was gentleness shown in your family as you grew up?**

2. **How did you and your parents express anger when you were growing up?**

3. **How do you handle anger today?**

4. What fears and insecurities lie behind your anger?

5. How did your family express love and attention?

6. How can recognizing the feeling behind your anger contribute to more gentleness in your life?

# RECOVERY GUIDE

But the fruit of the Spirit is . . . gentleness. (Galatians 5:22)

## Read Psalm 37:8–9.

1. In this psalm, David points out how people worry over the successes of evil men. Their fear and insecurity led to anger. What are you fretting about?

2. In what ways is your fretting or anger fueled by fear or insecurity?

3. How can you find your security in the Lord so that you can avoid reacting to life's circumstances with anger?

## Read Proverbs 29:11.

1. Anger itself is not sinful, but its expression can lead to sin. How has your anger led to sin?

**2. How have you channeled your anger in appropriate ways that lead to gentleness in situations and relationships?**

**Read James 1:19–21.**

In this passage, handling your anger gently is connected with humility. As you continue to display humility, you will become gentler. Humility will allow the Holy Spirit to work more freely in your life. Humility is a true evaluation of the self. It is thinking no more or less of yourself than you actually are (Romans 12:3).

**1. Have you talked with God about your anger? How willing are you to give your anger to him, trusting him to help you deal with your insecurities and fear?**

**2. Pray regularly, asking the Holy Spirit to help you become slow to anger. Ask the Spirit to develop within you the gentleness that leads to the "righteous life that God desires."**

## RECOVERY GOALS

Gentleness—that disposition of spirit Christ used to describe himself saying, "I am gentle and humble in heart" (Matt. 11:29). This gentleness spoken of in Scripture could also be translated "meekness." When people think of meekness, they often associate it with weakness. People think meek or gentle people are not able to do things for themselves. They wait for life to happen rather than make things happen.

But this perspective is not at all what Scripture refers to when it speaks of gentleness. Christ's gentleness flowed not from weakness but from strength. His gentleness came out of the power of God. As a Christian you can display gentleness because you have the power of God available to you. Your security comes from the resources available through the Lord. Anger robs God's Spirit from working.

1. List four recent situations in which you reacted with anger.

   •

   •

   •

   •

2. What are the common feelings behind your anger?

3. How could you express these feelings positively rather than cover them up with your anger?

4. How could the spirit of gentleness help you in these situations?

# 10.   I'm in the Driver's Seat: Self-Control

## RECOVERY FOCUS

- Examine your need to be in control.
- Recognize when you are attempting to control.
- Learn how to gain self-control in your life.

## RECOVERY INFORMATION

Growing up in a dysfunctional family with periodic or constant chaos placed you in an out-of-control situation. You never knew how things would be at home. You weren't sure when you arrived home if you would be greeted by a hug or a slap. You were often afraid to invite friends over because you never knew in what condition your parents would be. Or perhaps the chaos was more subtle. Your mother would at times be tender and kind but at other times she would be hysterical or verbally abusive.

You grew up feeling that your parents' behavior was somehow your fault. To retain your sense of dignity and self-respect, you developed coping mechanisms. You coped with your unpredictable parent or parents by learning to take charge of yourself and your environment. You vowed that you would never, ever be like your parents. "It won't happen to me" was your response. Since your parents were an unreliable source of trust and caring, you had to take control of every aspect of your life.

You learned to control other people, too, because it offered you a certain amount of consistency and a sense of relief from the desperation and anxiety you experienced. You learned fairly rigid rules for relating to others. This rigidity, which was a form of control, protected you from pain. The more out-of-control your parents became, the more obsessed you became with gaining control.

This dynamic still operates in your life today. When you feel desperate and anxious, you control.

You wear a mask called "in control." You present a façade that says you have your life together, that everything is okay. When things don't go the way you want them to in your life, you feel insecure and inadequate. You have learned that you can create security and adequacy in your life by controlling or at least trying to control the people and events around you.

## CONTROLLING YOUR FEELINGS

You grew up with the perception that feelings were bad or a sign of weakness. Showing emotions signaled a lack of control. So you pushed away your true feelings. What often popped up was anger. Anger is often the only feeling that is acceptable in dysfunctional families. In some families, not even anger can be shown.

Today your anger can be a real problem for you. If you could remove the mask of control, you would also see feelings of abandonment, shame, guilt, aloneness, fear, grief, rejection, hurt, confusion, inadequacy, or betrayal. Keeping your feelings hidden is a way of maintaining a sense of adequacy.

Rudy grew up in a tough family, and if he showed any sadness at all, his brother made fun of him. Rudy soon learned that the only way to survive was to be angry and tough, and he carried this response into his adult life. Whenever he felt sad, he masked his sadness with anger. When Rudy wanted his wife to pay more attention to him, he was unable to say he felt neglected. Instead, he would attack her verbally with criticism. Because he couldn't share his feelings, he didn't get what he wanted. Instead, Rudy's anger pushed his wife away, which only made him feel more isolated and angry.

## CONTROLLING YOUR PROBLEMS

When you admit you have problems, you admit that you are not in control. So you have learned to minimize your problems. Consequently, you have difficulty asking for and accepting advice and help from others.

Sandra led a Bible study for her church's women's ministry. One of the women in the study group talked one morning about some difficulties she was having in her marriage. The woman broke down and wept in front of the group as she told the group her husband had left her. Several other women shared personal difficulties and struggles they had encountered. Sandra shared how her successful marriage was a result of her trust in God.

Most of the women in the group knew that Sandra's husband rarely attended church. And they also knew he had a problem with alcohol. What they didn't know was that Sandra's husband was a full-blown alcoholic who had beaten her on several occasions. They didn't know about her father's drinking problems and the way he had physically abused her.

Sandra's life was progressively falling apart, but she had never shared these problems with the women in her group. She perceived that a self-disclosure of her family situation would make her more vulnerable to hurt and pain, something she felt she couldn't do. She felt she had to focus on what would offer victory and strength, which meant she denied her weaknesses. Sandra maintained what she thought was control of her life by keeping a big part of her life secret.

## CONTROLLING OTHERS

You control others anytime you attempt to manipulate what they do or who they are. Controlling others offers a sense of security. You can keep things going your way by conning, advising, giving ultimatums, intimidating, getting angry, taking charge, exploiting, maneuvering, criticizing, and using the people involved in your life.

Janet came to work and said her husband was leaving her. Her co-workers rallied around her, pouring out their sympathy. What actually had happened to Janet was that, after a marital fight, her husband had left to be alone for the afternoon. Janet exaggerated what happened to her as a way of controlling her co-workers' responses to her.

Tom could never relax in a group. The minute a meeting began at work, at church, or in a social gathering, Tom felt he had to keep things moving. "I always felt responsible for keeping everyone happy in the group. It was my way of staying in control of the group." This attitude led to a church burnout for Tom. He was so involved in all aspects of church life to maintain a sense of control over his spiritual life that he was used up by committees and teaching responsibilities. He left the church feeling hurt and angry.

## CONTROLLING EVENTS

Your need to control may also extend to manipulating events. Jonathon was concerned about being laid off at work. In order to feel in control of his work situation, he felt depressed. He had the mistaken belief that if he remained sad and depressed long enough, things would somehow change at work.

Linda, on the other hand, tried to control her work environment by pouring herself into her work. She felt that if she worked hard, her company would do well. But the plant where she worked went bankrupt, and Linda was laid off. She had to maintain the illusion of being in control even though her work had nothing to do with the plant closure.

## CONTROLLING GOD

At times you even try to control God. You do this by attempting to put God in a box. God must then work according to your agenda. In a warped kind of way, you try to make God "indebted" to you. You give him your time, energy, or money, and when he doesn't do what you want him to do, you feel ripped off.

When Lucia learned her mother had terminal cancer, Lucia began giving money to an evangelist, asking for healing for her mother. Lucia had to get a part-time job in addition to her day job to donate to the evangelist. When her mother died, Lucia was emotionally devastated. She expected God to heal her mother. Her control issues extended to her relationship with God. Lucia was not aware of her attempts at controlling God, but that's what her actions demonstrated. Her actions helped bolster her self-esteem. She gained a sense of power and control of her life through her actions toward God.

## A FALSE SENSE OF POWER

Your attempts to control your feelings, problems, relationships, events, as well as God provide you with a false sense of power. Your need for control really stems from your feelings of *powerlessness*. You are only fooling yourself when you believe you are in control of your life.

Your need to control is an indicator of how out-of-control your life really is. You can't successfully control your spouse, your children, your employer, or your friends. In working through this Recovery Discovery workbook, you have begun to admit this feeling of powerlessness. This admission is one of the first and biggest steps in your recovery.

Once you recognize that your need to control is really a signal that your life is out-of-control, where do you go from there? You fear that giving up control will just catapult your life into chaos. So what do you do?

## SURRENDER CONTROL TO GOD

The Christian is the only person who can afford to give up control. If you are a Christian, you can give your control issues to God. That doesn't mean you just give up. You consciously, intentionally surrender your issues to God, knowing that only he can sort out your life. Only he can give you the security that will give you the courage to give up control.

Giving up control doesn't mean you give up all responsibility. Growing up in a dysfunctional home has created confusion for you about responsibility. You often take responsibility for things that can only be God's responsibility, and you often neglect your personal responsibilities and blame God when things don't turn out right.

Juan was employed in a new job for only three weeks when he began to talk about getting a promotion. He talked and dreamed about a promotion. He prayed about a promotion. But he made no changes that would earn him the promotion. He expected it all to happen miraculously. He was trusting God for things he should have been doing. He needed to see his responsibility to work hard and pay his dues.

The more anxiety you experience in your life, the more likely you are to play God. When you begin experiencing anxiety, you need to let go of those things that you have no control over and work at those things over which you can exercise control and influence.

## CLUES TO CONTROL

Another step toward recovering from controlling behavior is to become more sensitive to that behavior when it surfaces in your life. Many indicators can give you clues about when you are attempting to control. We have outlined six indicators for you.

*Blame.* When you find yourself blaming others for what is happening in your life, you are probably attempting to control. When you blame others, you are saying that they—not you—are the ones who need to change. Pointing the finger gets you off the hook.

*Compulsive behavior.* When you have an urge to engage in compulsive behavior, you are attempting to control painful feelings and anxiety. Whether it is compulsive cleaning the house, running to the refrigerator for a bite to eat, smoking, drinking, gambling, or compulsive sexual behavior, compulsive behavior should send up a red flag.

*Childish thinking.* When you sustain a feeling in order to control people or events that are beyond your control, you are practicing a childish form of control. For instance, if you feel sad long enough, you feel that somebody (God) will help you. If you stay mad long enough, people will say they are sorry. Or if you feel confused long enough, somebody will rescue you.

*Stuffing feelings.* When you notice that you are denying feelings, you are engaging in controlling behavior. When you feel hurt by a friend but act as if everything is okay, when you are annoyed at your spouse but won't talk it out, or when you feel proud of your kids but can't tell them, you are controlling.

*Creating tension in others.* When people around you are anxious and tense, you may be trying to control them. Julia would become more domineering when her life became stressed. The more dominant she became, the more resistant and tense her family became. Once she was able to interpret family tension as a reflection of her controlling behavior, she was able to break her cycle of control.

*People pleasing.* Trying to make everybody happy is a sign that you are attempting to control. People pleasing is a strategy you have learned to eliminate the chaos in your life.

## RECOVERY PROBERS

1. When did you first realize you had a need to control?

2. What price have you paid for controlling your feelings?

3. How have you fooled yourself and others into thinking you have your problems under your control?

4. How do you manage your relationships so that you remain in control?

5. How do you attempt to manipulate events so that you feel you are in control of them?

6. How have you put God in a box to serve your hidden agenda?

7. What is your biggest fear when you consider giving up some of your control over your co-workers, spouse, children, friends, or God?

8. How have you confused God's responsibilities with your own?

9. Which of the clues (blame, compulsive behavior, childish thinking, stuffing your feelings, creating tension in others, or people pleasing) were helpful to you?

10. How can you use these clues to break your cycle of control?

## RECOVERY GUIDE

But the fruit of the Spirit is . . . self-control. (Galatians 5:22)

For the Christian, the issue of control is often confusing. Aren't Christians supposed to have self-control? We believe the Bible teaches that self-control means self *under* control, not self *in* control. God wants your will under the Holy Spirit's control; you want your will under your control. But self *in* control only creates problems. When you control, sin reigns in your life. It's only when you submit to God's control that you truly attain self-control. That's the paradox: when you surrender control of your self, you gain self-control.

## Read Psalm 6:6.

1. **List examples of how your attempts to control have created pain in your life.**

2. **List examples of how your controlling behaviors have been an obstacle to your growth as a Christian.**

## Read Romans 7:18–20.

Control is a dysfunctional behavior. As long as you believe the myth that you can control your life, your life will remain out-of-control.

1. **List examples of how your life appears to be within your control.**

2. **List examples of ways you maintain the façade of control in your life.**

3. List examples of ways you ignore your responsibilities in life and play God (a form of control).

4. List examples of how your life really is out-of-control.

**Read Matthew 6:10.**

1. Whose will do you want in your life?

2. What changes must you be willing to make if God's will is to have priority in your life?

3. What happens when you have attempted to control people and things?

4. What will happen if you live to do God's will in your life?

## RECOVERY GOALS

Facing your control issues requires a great deal of personal awareness about your controlling behaviors. List examples from your life of each of the following control indicators that you feel manifests itself in your life.

**Blame:**


**Compulsive behavior:**


**Childish thinking:**


**Stuffing your feelings:**


**Creating tension in others:**


**People pleasing:**

# LEADER'S GUIDE

## PURPOSE OF GROUP

Involve group members in defining this purpose so that they have some personal ownership in the group dynamic and can define some of their personal goals.

1. To provide people with the hope of recovery
2. To give information about growing up in an alcoholic or other dysfunctional family system
3. To assist adult children (of alcoholic or other dysfunctional families) in breaking the dysfunctional rules learned while growing up
4. To help adult children heal and grow
5. To point adult children to God for help
6. To encourage adult children to take responsibility for their personal recovery

## GROUP FORMAT

Suggested size of group: 8–12 members.

Suggested length of time for the group: 12–15 weeks, spending 1–2 hours per session.

### Opening Sessions

1. Define the purpose of the group and ask why people are there.
2. Read together the Group Ground Rules, found on the following pages.
3. Ask each person to take 10–15 minutes to give his or her personal background and tell his or her story.
4. Define your expectations of attendance and workbook involvement. Get clear commitments from group members.
5. Establish a support network for the group members. Talk about meeting outside the group for coffee, exchange phone numbers, and the like.

### Workbook Sessions

1. Open each session with prayer, asking for God's presence to protect and lead the group.

2. Share victories, especially those related to previous chapters. Encourage people to share goals they have met.
3. Discuss the various sections of the week's workbook chapter, asking questions about the Recovery Information and using the questions in the Recovery Probers and Recovery Guide for group discussion.
4. Share current struggles. Allow people time to work on struggles.
5. Pray together each week.
6. If you feel comfortable, involve group members in role playing. Come with a prepared situation you want them to role play or talk about, or give group members freedom to practice on situations from their own families.

### Closing Sessions

1. Focus on what has been gained by reflecting on victories.
2. Talk about what relationships have been meaningful.
3. Make a commitment to have a reunion in three months.
4. Talk about where people can now find support.

## GROUP GROUND RULES

1. All conversations in the group are confidential and may not be shared with anyone outside the group. If permission is asked and everyone is comfortable, an exception can be made. Protection leading to trust building is a goal of this group.
2. These groups aren't open groups, which means that others can't be invited after the group starts. There can be exceptions if the group and the group leader agree.
3. It is important that people share what they are experiencing and that they don't generalize. They need to own their own feelings and not judge others. For example, say "I have a difficult time trusting people" rather than "You can't trust anyone these days."
4. Members aren't responsible for other members; group members are not responsible to give advice, excuse other people's actions, minimize other's feelings, or fix hurting people. What this means is there is no cross-talk allowed. Group members may share experience from their point of view if someone in the group needs that information.
5. Listen without interrupting, unless you are the leader and

responsible to watch the time in sharing. Each person's story and experience is valuable. Each group member is valuable.

6. Avoid using "shoulds" or "oughts" in the group, either for yourself or others.

7. If a group member becomes anxious about the group experience, talk about it in the group. If a group member wants to quit the group over fearful feelings or resentment, talk about it in the group. Do a reality check with the person, helping him or her to see if the fear is warranted or just a part of the recovery process. Honesty is a key to successful recovery. And honesty can be practiced at times like this in the group.

8. Stay on the goals and purposes of the group and keep conversations directed.

9. Make and express additional ground rules that would make this group a more effective place for recovery to occur.

## GROUP PROCESS

Groups form in stages. The initial stage is one of bonding, a stage in which group members share about themselves and find out if the group is safe. The leader's role is to facilitate safety and openness. Leaders need to work toward giving everyone the opportunity to share. Be careful not to allow group members to try to rescue each other.

In later stages, the group members will jockey for positions. Don't be surprised if group members challenge your leadership and some members re-create in the group their dysfunctional behaviors. The issue of control can become a primary issue in this group. Your role is to avoid thinking like a rescuer or a victim and to move the group and its members toward personal responsibility, godliness, and healthy thinking. This gives opportunity for real dialogue between group members and for teaching of new skills.

In the last stages, group members need to learn to let go and say good-by in a healthy way. Help group members to focus on what they have learned and how they have grown. Help group members reflect on their victories and express their joy from relationships. Your role will be one of helping members not to rationalize but to face their feelings and examine their adult-child self-defeating attitudes and behaviors.

# REFERRALS

Adult children of alcoholic or other dysfunctional families often experience depression, grief, and high levels of anxiety. Any signs of deep depression such as insomnia, significant weight loss or weight gain, withdrawal from life tasks, or suicidal thoughts must be referred to a pastor, counseling professional, or hospital. Other issues may arise that would call for referrals. When developing a referral list, consider:

1. Caring churches that minister to people
2. Treatment centers
3. Christian counselors
4. Social service agencies

## SUGGESTED QUALIFICATIONS FOR GROUP LEADERS

For maximum effectiveness, leaders will have

1. attended a recovery program like Codependents Anonymous, Adult Children of Alcoholics, or Al-Anon for a year or more.
2. achieved and maintained some emotional sobriety and stability with their adult-child issues.
3. been a Christian for several years and have a basic knowledge of the Bible.
4. a dynamic relationship with Christ and a commitment to pray daily for their group members.
5. experience in facilitating a group. If possible, leaders will first serve as co-leaders of a group before having primary leadership responsibilities.
6. experience teaching and practicing basic communication skills, like "using 'I messages,'" "reflective listening," "problem ownership," "setting boundaries," and the like.
7. accountability to the leaders of the facility in which the support group meets. For instance, if the group meets in a church and is sanctioned by the church, support-group leaders will be accountable to the church's leadership.
8. wisdom on knowing when to refer group members for professional help.
9. Christ-centered motives for leading a group.
10. no anxiety about strong expressions of emotion.
11. demonstrated diligence in working through his or her own adult-child issues.

# SUGGESTED READINGS

If you found this Recovery Discovery workbook helpful, you may also find help from the following books:

Black, Claudia. *It Will Never Happen to Me!: Children of Alcoholics As Youngsters, Adolescents, Adults*. Denver: M. A. C. Printing and Publications Division, 1981.

Cermak, Timmen. *A Primer on Adult Children of Alcoholics*. Deerfield Beach, Florida: Health Communications, Inc., 1989.

Friends in Recovery. *The Twelve Steps—A Spiritual Journey: A Working Guide for Adult Children from Addictive and Other Dysfunctional Families*. San Diego: Recovery Publications, 1988.

Friends in Recovery. *The Twelve Steps for Christians from Addictive and Other Dysfunctional Families*. San Diego: Recovery Publications, 1988.

Grayson, Curt, and Johnson, Jan. *Creating a Safe Place: Christians Healing from the Hurt of Dysfunctional Families*. San Francisco: Harper & Row, 1991.

Guernsey, Dr. Dennis, and Guernsey, Lucy. *Birth Marks: Breaking Free from the Destructive Imprints of Your Family History*. Waco, Tex.: Word Publishing, 1991.

Ross, Ron. *When I Grow Up, I Want to Be an Adult: Christ-Centered Recovery for Adult Children*. San Diego: Recovery Publications, 1990.

Woititz, Janet Geringer. *Adult Children of Alcoholics*. Deerfield Beach, Florida: Health Communications, Inc., 1990.